YEARS
OF HOPE

Konstantin Paustovsky

THE STORY OF A LIFE

YEARS

OF HOPE

TRANSLATED FROM THE RUSSIAN
BY MANYA HARARI AND ANDREW THOMSON

PANTHEON BOOKS
A Division of Random House, New York

Contents

I

Forerunners of Ostap Bender

In a piercing north wind, on a February day in 1920, the Whites fled from Odessa, firing a few parting shots at the town; the shells burst in the sky with a faint crump.

They left behind them a devastated city. The wind blew armfuls of half-burnt papers and greasy Denikin notes along the streets, piling them up against the drainpipes. The notes were worthless – they wouldn't have bought an olive. People simply threw them away. The shops shut down. Through the windows you could see swarms of ginger wharf-rats feverishly searching the dusty counters. The busy market squares had turned into deserts of cobblestone. Only the cats, unsteady with hunger, wandered about looking for scraps. But scraps in Odessa were a thing of the past.

Every last remnant of food had vanished. It was blood-chilling to think that all you could get in the whole enormous sea-port town was a little water tasting of rust. Miraculously, the pumps were still working and brought a trickle of it from the Dniester.

I had been living in Dr Landeman's disused sanatorium in Black Sea Street. Several journalists had moved in with me, among them Yasha Lifshitz, an extremely active reporter from Petrograd, who was interested in nothing but politics and his work. I spoke of him in the preceding volume of my autobiography, *In that Dawn*.

Shortly before the Soviet troops arrived, Yasha told me we ought to clear out, as the Bolsheviks were sure to nationalise the sanatorium and would turn us out anyway.

'We might get into serious trouble,' Yasha announced in a voice of doom.

He didn't say what kind of trouble, and as we were all expecting trouble all the time I didn't bother to ask him.

Yasha and I found a porter's lodge in the same street and rented it from the enterprising landlord, an unfrocked priest called Prosvirnyak.

The lodge stood in a neglected garden surrounded by high walls of rough stone, at the back of a two-storeyed building facing the street. In those unquiet days it was as peaceful there as in a fortress. Prosvirnyak himself had named the lodge 'Fort Monte Cristo'.

The previous tenant had been a Russianised German, Schwittau, a professor of political economy at the University of Novorossisk. He had converted the house into a comfortable villa, surrounded it with beds of marguerites and moved his library into it, but he soon felt a foreboding of danger and, forsaking all, fled to Constantinople.

The Professor's library consisted almost entirely of German books on economics, so tidy that they might never have been opened. Partly for this reason and partly too because of their Gothic script, I imagined them to be ineffably boring.

The books gave out a sharp smell of lysol and cloves. Ever since, these smells have been for me a sign of paralysing boredom, especially the smell of cloves; seeds of some tropical plant, they look like black carpet-tacks.

On the other hand, standing on the Professor's shelves were all eighty-six volumes of Brockhaus and Efron's Encyclopaedic Dictionary, and this was treasure indeed.

Living among his possessions, I formed a mental picture of the Professor. He was smug, well-washed, pink, with a reddish beard and gold-rimmed glasses, and his eyes had the watery gleam you often see in those of ageing bachelors. I disliked this image of my predecessor, so I kept the windows wide open, hoping that his staid ghost would be blown away.

Before describing the events that followed, I should say something about Black Sea Street. I grew very fond of this small suburban street and believed it to be the most picturesque in the world.

Even the way to it from town was a tonic against adversity, as I often experienced. I might be walking home, utterly dejected by some failure, but as soon as I found myself in the deserted alleyways around Black Sea Street – Observatory Lane, Sturzo Lane, Battery Lane – and heard the rustling of the old acacia trees, saw the ivy dark on walls gilded by the winter sun, felt the breath of the sea on my face, I at once recovered my peace of mind and lightness of heart.

These alleys all ran between garden walls; the houses hid at the back of the gardens, behind locked wicket-gates. The alleys led to Black Sea Street, and Black Sea Street stretched along the edge of the cliffs overhanging the sea – though 'stretched' is perhaps the wrong word: it was so short that you could walk from one end to the other of it in a few minutes.

The street was open to the sea, which was beautiful in all weather. On the left, you looked down on Langeron and Quarantine Harbour, where an old pier, worn smooth by the storms, curved out to sea. On the right, the steep rust-red cliffs, overgrown with pigsweed and goosefoot, led to Arcadia and the Fountains, towards the misty beaches on which the tides would often wash up floating mines, torn from their moorings.

Black Sea Street was the naval outpost of Odessa. All the steamers passed it on their way to and from the port. The rustling of its gardens told us the varying strength of the wind; we learned to gauge it by this sound as sailors do by the Beaufort Scale.

There were other, slighter sounds as well, that served as weather signs. The drumming of ripe chestnuts on the pavements meant that the wind was freshening and had reached gale force four.

Black Sea Street was always empty. Its few inhabitants preferred to stay indoors. The day the coalman passed with his horse and cart, we could hardly believe our eyes – firstly because charcoal was worth its weight in gold, and also because the coalman was fearlessly advertising his status as a private trader by actually shouting in his rich and sombre voice the welcome words: 'Charcoal! Lovely charcoal!'

In those comfortless days, Black Sea Street seemed, however deceptively, an island of salvation for those who had been washed up on it by the storms of life.

Those were the days when Ilya Arnoldovich Ilf,[1] long before he became a writer, went about Odessa in a shabby cloak and with a step ladder, doing electrical repairs. His ladder over his shoulder, he looked like the tall, thin chimneysweep in Hans Anderson's fairytale.

Ilf was an electrician. He took his time over his repairs. Perched on his ladder, his pince-nez glinting, he kept a sharp eye on what was happening in the noisy flats and offices at his feet.

He evidently found much that was comic, for although he kept quiet about it, he was always chuckling to himself.

Dozens of Ostap Benders,[2] as yet undescribed and unrevealed, sauntered past him. They took little notice of him except for cracking an occasional joke about his 'intellectual' glasses and turned-up trousers. But they did occasionally offer him a little hydrochloric acid (of which the very existence had been long forgotten) for his soldering iron, or three yards of flex pinched from a synagogue.

Ilf would bargain long and furiously, with the sole object of hearing the latest Odessa jokes, sayings and swear-words. The fashion in them was always changing. It depended on a number of things – the position on the front in the Civil War, the presence or absence in Constantinople of the British Dreadnaught *Superb,* the behaviour of the Baltic sailors billeted on the miller, Weinstein. The latest expression, 'May I never get to where I'm going', plainly hinted at the danger of walking about the Odessa streets.

Ilf had soon to look for another job, for the power-station broke down – the Odessans thought, for good.

What has made me think of him and of his hero, the fearless racketeer Ostap Bender, is that even in those grim days racketeering flourished in Odessa. Even the most spineless caught the infection. They, too, came to believe in the ancient law of the junk-market: 'If you want to eat, know how to sell the sleeves of a waistcoat.'

In time, the rackets infiltrated even our literary and journalistic milieu.

Neither Yasha nor I had a kopeck of Soviet money. We had enough salt fish for one day, and two stale rusks lying in the drawer of the desk. They gave out the same abominable smell of cloves and lysol as the Professor's books.

We knew we should do something if we were not to starve to death, but neither of us could think of anything. Anyway, what could you do in a half-ruined town in which there were as yet no offices, newspapers, markets, and indeed no Soviet money! You could only wait for things to settle down. Yet how could we wait when we were already faint and sick with hunger?

So we lay on our bunks, our threadbare coats over our heads, and all the same waited for something.

The lodge was like an ice-box. We stoked our *bourzhouika* stove[3] with newspapers and it quickly became red-hot. But it cooled down just as soon.

On the fifth day of the Soviet occupation of Odessa, we were visited by my old school friend from Kiev, Volodya Golovchiner. I had run into him a fortnight earlier in Deribasov Street where, in spite of his weak eyesight, gold-rimmed spectacles and seedy but lordly appearance, he was carrying on a brisk trade in cigarette lighters.

Volodya brought with him a little man, wrinkled as a monkey, who spoke very fast and as indistinctly as though his mouth were full of pebbles.

'This' – Volodya pointed vaguely in his direction – 'is Comrade Torelli, an Odessa reporter. Torelli is his pseudonym. "In the world," as your unfrocked landlord would say, his name is Blumkis. He has an idea.'

We poked our heads from under our coats and looked in silence at the owner of the idea, who was smiling guiltily.

'Torelli or Toricelli?' Yasha asked querulously. He was hard of hearing.

'Torelli,' Volodya said gloomily. 'But that's not the point. His idea has a bearing on our wretched circumstances. The said Comrade Torelli, Blumkis in the world, is in the same unenviable situation as the two of you and even I, Volodya Golovchiner, a champion swimmer and the son of a Kharkov professor of stomatology. He will explain his plan to you himself – in so far as his linguistic abilities will allow.'

Volodya was fond of talking in riddles. I remembered this from our schooldays.

Torelli rattled off something that sounded like a rapid roll on a bass drum.

'Allow me,' Volodya said impassively. 'I'll translate. Comrade Torelli believes that his idea should be adopted at once and, if possible, taken seriously.'

It turned out that Torelli was a lodger in Prosvirnyak's two-storeyed house, the one facing the street. He had heard from Prosvirnyak that we were 'metropolitan' journalists. Torelli envied metropolitan journalists, although nothing in the world would have induced him to leave Odessa even for a job on the *Russian Word*.[4] You may well ask why. The answer is simple. In Odessa you could always 'create' a sensation. You could write in the *Odessa Post*, for instance, that a meridian had exploded in the suburb of Perekop, and only the heroic efforts of the fire brigade had prevented loss of life among the working population. In Moscow or Petrograd, you could never get away with anything like that.

But this was not the point now, said Torelli. The point was how to survive. For this, at least four experienced journalists must combine their efforts. His idea entailed a certain risk, but if it succeeded we would have bread to eat the very next day, and perhaps even an advance of several 'lemons' each. Lemons were Soviet million rouble notes.

He refused to say what the idea was. We would have to trust him.

'It's unlucky to say too much in advance,' he told us firmly.

We were ready to believe anything. We were past caring. What was a risk more or less in our circumstances? We agreed to everything.

'Good,' said Torelli. 'Then I'll come for you tomorrow at eight.'

He put on his battered straw hat – until then he had been holding it behind his back – playfully said 'ta-ta!' and vanished.

'That's how it is,' Yasha said thoughtfully. 'All gone in the mighty storm. Everything sold for food.'

'What are you talking about?' asked Volodya.

'The fact that Comrade Torelli's boater is not the headgear for Odessa's winter winds.'

'He's got a sister, you know,' said Volodya. 'Last year she became paralysed, she can't walk. They live in one room. You can't imagine how devotedly he looks after her. Beneath that pitiful exterior beats a generous heart – a theme fit for Shakespeare!'

'What's he up to, your Torelli?' asked Yasha. 'He won't land us in some idiotic mess?'

Volodya said that everything was possible, and left us. We pulled our coats over our heads again. But for a long time I could not get warm and go to sleep.

I awoke at dawn when the air outside looked like muddy water tinted with aquamarine. Even to the eye, it was coarse-grained and laden with an icy wind. The wind was evidently blowing straight from the Pole. I thought disgustedly of having to get up and go out, and of how the wind would get inside my collar and numb my spine.

Why not stay at home? Curl up under my coat, gather all my warmth and, dozing off, extract from it, as from the cotton wool on a Christmas tree, a delicate, spun-glass dream, blue and gay and leaving behind it the same impression of tenderness as you get from kissing a sleeping child.

I waited for such a dream, but heard instead the angry hiss of the wind in the garden. Through it came after a while the sound of loud, insistent knocking – Torelli had arrived.

We walked to town through Alexander Park. The north wind lashed our faces with gravel and whipped up the gritty dust. The zinc-coloured sea rolled muddy waves, thundering out of the zinc-coloured morning mist. The persistent grating of the zinc vane on the roof of the small observatory in the park set one's teeth on edge.

'The spring will never come,' said Yasha. 'The sun will never shine. There will never again be anything. To think otherwise is the illusion of doomed intellectuals.'

Torelli gave a squeak and a cough. After a moment I realised that he was laughing. Reddish tears shone in his wind-beaten eyes.

'Where are you taking us?' Yasha asked him suspiciously. 'All this will end in a mess. I feel it in my bones.'

'Only to the nearest Soviet institution in Odessa, I swear it,' Torelli said hastily. 'There must be one that's opened by now. And you did say you were willing to take a risk.'

Volodya Golovchiner was waiting for us at the corner of Kanatny Street.

The town was empty. Horsemen with red ribbons on worn sheepskin hats clattered down the street, passing us without a glance. From every gateway, little boys popped out, and immediately, powerful maternal voices echoed through the yards:

'Back, you little pests. Come back at once!'

Shaking the windows, a lorry with a load of broken furniture rumbled slowly past. A soldier with a rifle sat in the back, smoking. The small boys reappeared in the gateways and disappeared as suddenly to renewed shrieks of, 'Come back, you bastards, may you burn in hell!'

The wonderful, stimulating smell of cheap tobacco drifted down the street. It made my mouth water.

'Keep up with that lorry,' Torelli whispered crossly. 'That's our chance.'

We quickened our pace. The lorry turned into Richelieu Street, towards the Opera House, and stopped in front of a dark grey building. It was one of the buildings left over from the time of Richelieu and De Ribas which gave Odessa the noble features of

Genoa, Florence and, according to some Odessans, of Paris .tself.[5]

Piled up on the pavement, in front of the classical façade, were all the normal fittings of an average Soviet government department (this one, evidently, spent most of its time on the road): torn paper rolls, faded posters on calico wrapped round poles, rickety desks, dithering book-cases that fall on their faces at the slam of a door, portraits in grey frames, a dented boiler, and a mass of wooden boxes.

All this property was guarded by a sailor with a head of ginger hair so wiry that his cap seemed to float in the air above it.

Nailed to the door of the building was a piece of canvas with the inscription: 'Odessa Oprodkomgub'.

'This way, quick!' said Torelli. He dashed round the corner and reappeared in the small Palais-Royal Square beside the Opera House, where the sailor couldn't see us.

No longer the pitiful figure of the day before or even of the past hour, Torelli's face glowed with inspiration – I could not imagine why – and his eyes glinted craftily through the slits between his puffy eyelids.

'The first thing is to find out what Oprodkomgub stands for,' he said.

As it happened I knew that the abbreviation stood for 'Special Regional Rationing Committee'.

Torelli slapped his knees with his bony little hands and gave a stifled giggle.

'What could be better! It's exactly what we want!'

This was more than Volodya Golovchiner could stomach.

'Listen to me, Signor Torelli, either you tell us exactly what all this nonsense is about, or we leave you here and now and go home.'

It was then that Torelli told us his 'idea', his plan, and it struck us as both incredibly stupid and incredibly dangerous.

'You know what a government department is like,' he asked us, 'or don't you? You know that no self-respecting department can keep going without publishing an information leaflet or a bulletin of some sort about its work? Even the poorest has its information office. You do realise that? Right. But have you thought that to have an information office it needs journalists? Especially reporters. And that unless he has such an office, the head of the department – be he Mr Ford himself – gets bogged down in his work like a chicken in a puddle? We'll start an information office for Oprodkomgub! We'll print a lovely report about the arrival in Odessa of three barrels of smoked fish from Ochakov and a wagon-load of maize and tomatoes from Tiraspol for immediate distribution to the citizens. And you know what this means for Odessa? It means that life will begin! – Life!' he shouted.

'And how can you be sure that they haven't got an information office?' asked Yasha. 'You take too much on yourself, Comrade Toricelli.'

'Ha! Ha-ha! Twenty times ha-ha! Can't you see they haven't even stowed their rubbish yet? They haven't started, they're infants! But suppose they do have an information office, well, they aren't the only department in Odessa. We'll go to another and start one there.'

Crushed by his logic, we could think of nothing to say.

'What it needs is a solid-looking character in spectacles who speaks Russian like the actor Kachalov,' said Torelli. 'You'll do very well, Comrade Golovchiner. You'll be the head of the section. You,' pointing at me, 'deputy; you, Comrade Lifshitz – treasurer, and I'll be the reporter. But what we have to do now is slip past that ginger Goliath of a sailor with his rifle. Come on, quick! The worst thing on this kind of job is to hang about.'

We assumed a business-like air and went up to the door of the enigmatic Oprodkomgub. Torelli followed, hiding behind our backs and whistling out of tune.

The sailor sat on a packing case, holding a small shaggy white dog by the front paws.

'Beg for uncle,' he was growling at it. 'Beg for uncle, you shaggy devil! You poor old toots, you! Come on, beg!'

The little dog wagged its tail and yelped, clearly unused to such flattering treatment. But it couldn't beg.

'Strayed out of the night,' the sailor told us. 'And now he won't go. Such a well-behaved little dog, you wouldn't believe it!

He's hungry, the brute. We'll have to put him on the strength, that's what we'll have to do,' he ruffled the dog's fur affectionately. 'We'll have to take him on, the wicked old thing. Fancy putting such a shaggy hound on a sailor's rations!'

The dog thrashed with its tail and howled with delight.

We slipped past the sailor, under the grim vaults of Oprodkomgub. I looked at my companions. They were smiling sheepishly.

'Quite a lad, that,' Yasha said unexpectedly.

'Who do you mean?' asked Torelli.

'Certainly not you.'

Tramping in heavy boots, soldiers were dragging office furniture along dark corridors. Cupboard doors flew open and crashed shut. The soldiers swore in muffled voices.

'Well, now,' said Volodya Golovchiner. 'We find out which of these rooms is the office of the head of the department, and we go and ask him to take us on.'

Torelli threw up his hands, stepped back and looked at him in horror and contempt.

'What are you talking about?' he hissed. 'Have you gone completely off your head? Or what? Are you a child? Do you want us sent straight to the Cheka[6] and liquidated? We walk in from the street and – bang! – we call on the department head! Who are we? What are we? Gutter journalists? The yellow press? You'll be the death of us. A lot of good I did, sweating out a brilliant plan for you to finish us all off! Is that how you go about things?'

'How, then?' We were all taken aback.

'If you don't know, then leave it to me,' Torelli said haughtily. 'I'll tell you what to do. No heads! We are the heads! Follow me.'

Bitterly regretting that we had ever got mixed up with him, we followed nervously.

Fortunately, no one took any notice of us and we eventually found ourselves in an empty, unswept corridor on the first floor. At the far end were the back-stairs and a lavatory, its door broken off its hinges.

'This looks all right,' said Torelli, pushing open the nearest door. It led into a room with nothing in it except vaccination forms lying on the floor, and a poster saying: 'Fight Swine Trachinosis!'

Torelli picked up the poster, laid it face-down on the window-sill and, taking a blue pencil from his pocket, wrote in an ornate hand: 'Information Section'. He thought a little and added in smaller script: 'Section Head Golovchiner V.L.'

We watched him, spellbound like rabbits by a rattle snake.

He reached into his trouser pocket for an envelope with a few tacks in it, went outside and pinned the poster to the door.

'That's that,' he said, rubbing his hands cheerfully. 'All according to plan. End of Act One. Now we await developments. Be seated, pray, on the windowsills.'

Volodya Golovchiner had a packet of Cuban tobacco, dry and black as peat. We sat down on the dusty windowsills, lit cigarettes and waited, talking in whispers – all except Torelli who whistled the waltz from the *Merry Widow*.

'Who knows,' Yasha said doubtfully. 'They might really shoot us, at that.'

Torelli snorted with contempt.

We sat and listened to the random sounds that gradually filled the building. There even came, like a summons from the underworld, the cracked tinkle of a telephone.

Through the window we could see the slope of Langeron. The wind was falling and the sea turning blue.

'We are impostors,' Yasha said gloomily. 'They'll see through us in no time. Why don't we go before it's too late?'

Torelli turned on him. 'I like that! Bravo! Encore! Don't make me laugh! Where's the imposture? Aren't we going to do an honest job of work? We are intellectuals and we are looking for a place where we can make ourselves useful. Isn't that just plain commonsense?'

'Torelli, you are a genius!' said Volodya. 'A Herbert Spencer, a Kant, a Poincaré! You have put my shaky status as future head of

the information section on a solid basis. Now I feel I'm growing
wings!'

'Quiet!' Yasha suddenly said in an angry whisper, 'Stop fooling.
Someone's coming.'

Indeed, from the corridor came the sound of footsteps and the
clanking of spurs. The footsteps had the iron ring of the Com-
mendatore's. The owner of the spurs stopped outside our door,
coughed loudly, waited, and flung the door open. We shuddered.

Standing in the doorway was, all too obviously, a desperado in
command of one of the famous partisan units. Shaggy thick grey
eyebrows jutted out over his soot-black eyes. Blue shadows lay on
his cheeks. A powerful Mauser with a wooden butt hung from his
belt, and a map case was slung over his shoulder. The pockets of
his field jacket bulged with cartridges, tobacco, flints and crumpled
paper money. Crammed with all these things, both pockets had
cracked at the seams and at each of his movements spilled handfuls
of the precious tobacco.

The man with the Mauser looked us over carefully, then,
glancing round the room and sizing it up, said in an unexpectedly
high piping voice:

'Hullo to you. I am Karp Polikarpovich Karpenko. Former
worker in the field of education, now your Commandant. Which
of you is the head of this remarkable section? I understand his
name is Golovchiner V. L. Is he here?'

'Yes, it's me,' Volodya cautiously replied.

'In that case,' said the Commandant, 'I humbly beg you to
produce within the hour a detailed and signed list of all your
requirements. And don't wait for other sections to get in first.
The information section is always left in the lurch, as I know from
long experience. And you know why? Because, dear Comrade
Golovchiner, intellectuals dither and whine over every bit of
rubbish. You have to show teeth and claws. Like that.' The
Commandant showed us his hairy red fist, he even turned it this
way and that so that we should see it better. 'As the saying goes,
spin it round a hundred times and strike once. Then all the
grunting stops and there's order. And there's this little thing as

well,' he tapped his Mauser, 'to clear the brain better than smelling
salts. So, don't worry. I'll look after you, in as much as I've
inherited a respect for worker intellectuals from my father. It's
quite true, you know, what the poet says about sowing wisdom,
goodness and eternal values. . . .'

He broke off and listened. Several men were groaning outside
the door. He flung it open, dashed out and screamed in a tearful,
old woman's voice:

'Are you crazy? What's this circus act? Can't you see it's the
Information Section? What does it want with the fireproof safe
that's meant for Accounts? Take it back. Down the back stairs to
the ground floor. Shaking the whole building, you devils, cracking
floorboards like china! Honest to God, it makes me sick just to
look at you!'

There was puffing and panting outside the door, then a crash.
Something fell, the window frame cracked, the glass flew tinkling,
and the Commandant shouted desperately once again (as people
usually shout when they clutch their heads):

'Hold it! Hold it, the devil, or you'll bring down the whole
building! Hold it, I tell you. . . .'

It was then we felt the first tremor as of an earthquake. The
building shuddered and swayed. Something thundered from the
first to the ground floor. The attic shook overhead and ceiling
plaster came down in a shower of white scales. Boots thudded
outside, as people scattered.

The sound of the second shock merged with the Commandant's
hoarse howl:

'Get off the landing, you bastards! Can't you see what's
happening? Get off!'

The earthquake ceased as suddenly as it had begun. We went
out into the corridor. Plaster dust hung like thick fog. The floor
was furrowed as though a heavy plough had been at work on it.
A corner was knocked off the window. At the foot of the back
stairs lay the wretched steel safe, enmeshed in broken ropes and
resting on its side after its leap from the first floor. The railing of
the stairs, snapped clean off, hung miraculously by a rusty wire.

Forerunners of Ostap Bender

Around the safe, as around a corpse, the soldier-porters stood dejected, heads bowed. They were evidently a fatigue squadron and looked anything but soldierly.

Deep in thought, the Commandant also stood beside the safe. He saw us and kicked it with the toe of his boot. The spur jangled crossly.

'Seen the brute? A real killer! So you'll send me your list, Comrade Golovchiner. And don't be shy, ask for all you need.'

At that moment we became convinced that Torelli's 'brilliant' plan had succeeded, if not completely, at least in part.

We compiled the list and Torelli took it to the Commandant. He also had a friendly talk with him and learnt something of the way of life of Oprodkomgub. The Commandant was 'all right', Torelli told us.

We cheered up, especially when the first chairs and desks appeared in our room. Even Yasha brightened up. He stopped croaking, though he occasionally reminded us of the grim hour still to come, when we would have to fill in forms.

But our troubles were not over yet. Once more there were footsteps in the corridor, this time of several people. We quickly sat down at our desks, on which there wasn't yet so much as an inkwell.

Once again the door was flung open, and there came in a weedy young man in a coat altered from an army great-coat, a student's faded cap on his head. He peered at us shortsightedly through his thick spectacles.

This was Comrade Agin, former law student from Kharkov and now head of Oprodkomgub.

He was followed by his retinue – a bunch of hefty lads in tight tunics with creaky leather sword-belts.

It looked like the arrival of the Emperor Marcus Aurelius – a lofty-minded poet and philosopher – surrounded by legionaries clattering with armour and swords.

For a long time it was to seem to us incredible that this mild and sickly man could run the department responsible for Odessa's food supplies, a rough and noisy place which was at once besieged by every shady dealer, thug and racketeer in town, all trying to breach its defences. But Agin, though quiet, was firm as a rock, and the seething crowds of red-faced speculators, on fire with dreams of fabulous profits, were stilled like waves at the door of his office.

'So we even have an information section!' Agin chewed his lips thoughtfully, and smiled.

My heart sank.

He looked at each of us in turn and grinned again.

'Who is the head of the section? You, Comrade? Glad to meet you. Your name? Golovchiner? No relation of the well known Zionist? No? Just as well. Even namesakes can be a nuisance. And these are your colleagues? All journalists? Very glad indeed. I hope we'll work in together, though at present the function of your section is not altogether clear to me.'

Torelli emitted a prolonged and indistinct sound, presumably to the effect that we would certainly work in.

Agin turned to him, his head slightly to one side, as though pondering this flood of eloquence and awaiting its continuation. But Torelli broke into a sweat and kept quiet.

'Yes, I see,' said Agin with a friendly smile. 'Of course, you are quite right.'

He asked Volodya to come to his office to attend a meeting of heads of sections, nodded to the rest of us, and left.

Volodya's face was white as a sheet.

He was away two hours – we were in agony – and came back, pink and jolly, said, 'Cheer up!' and handed us each a hundred thousand roubles, a bread card, and a form with a hundred and twenty questions to answer. But forms no longer frightened us. We showered congratulations and thanks on Torelli. Radiant as a conqueror, he kissed us thrice in the Moscow manner.

By the evening, the room really looked like a newspaper office. A small new rotary press stood on a table. On the wall above it hung an enormous poster of a green-helmeted Red soldier sticking his bayonet into the belly of a scaly dragon. A shaggy purple

22

flame came from the dragon's mouth. The caption read: 'Down with the hydra of counter-revolution!'

Over Volodya Golovchiner's desk hung a sheet of cardboard. On it were printed the portraits of the leaders, each in a small circle of oak-leaves. The faces were all, mysteriously, as alike as peas. The reason was that the watery ink had run and all the features had smudged into a blur.

The posters had been sent us as a sign of special favour by Karp Polikarpovich Karpenko.

Life was once more beautiful and the bread, warm from the temporary bakery next door, unusually tasty. Never before had I eaten such fragrant bread with such a crisp crust.

Everything had gone off splendidly, but all the same Yasha and I felt uneasy in our heart of hearts and one night, as he lay tossing on his bare bunk, he said to me:

'I don't know about you, but I've decided to go to Agin and make a clean breast of it about how we got into Oprodkomgub.'

'All right. We'll both go.'

Next morning we went. That day, for the first time, there were signs of spring. The sun was stronger, and white clouds, tumbling apart to reveal blue depths of sky, sailed over the sea.

You could feel the spring even in Agin's office. The damp floorboards steamed where patches of sunlight fell on them through the window.

Sitting back in his armchair, Agin heard us out politely, nodded, and laughed.

'I was expecting you,' he said, 'but to be honest, not quite so soon. I knew all about it. I can't say I was carried away by your manoeuvre; it bordered on criminal practice. Though, as it wasn't you who thought it up – it was that little man with the wrong Italian name – you haven't much to reproach yourselves with. Still, I wouldn't be much good as a department head if I hadn't realised there was something fishy.'

'How did you guess?' asked Yasha.

'There was no information section allowed for in the plan. It appeared out of the blue. Karp Polikarpovich got suspicious at once. But he said you looked like educated people, certainly not crooks, probably good at your job, so it was a pity to sink you by having a row. I admit, though, it wasn't easy for me to include your improvised section retrospectively in the structure of the department. The oddest thing is that we do need such a section, as it turns out. We would be much worse off without it. So I am duly grateful.'

2

Plywood Maze

The old acacia trees in the boulevards flowered, and everything around them was strewn with yellowish blossoms.

In the thick of the acacias stood the Northern Hotel, to which Oprodkomgub moved in spring.

During the early revolutionary years, government departments showed an extraordinary restlessness. They were always on the move from one building to another, which they took over to the accompaniment of much noise, and immediately filled with flimsy plywood partitions and equally flimsy doors.

Set end to end, the partitions from any one department could easily have walled the city along the line of the Portofrank Circular Road.

Never quite reaching the ceiling, the partitions crossed at fanciful angles, cut stair-landings in half and formed dark, mysterious alleyways and dead-ends.

A vertical cross-section of the building from attic to basement would have revealed an astonishingly intricate human ant-hill inhabited by a unique species of human ant. They scribbled their way through mountains of paper by day and hid them for the night in the plywood cells with which the hill was honeycombed.

It was customary to plaster the partitions all over with orders, notices and wall-newspapers the size of bed-sheets.

A zinc tub for drinking water, with a tin mug attached by a chain, was set up in the plywood corridor; Aunt Motya or Aunt

Raya, the messenger woman, sat beside it; from that moment, the department became fully operational.

It sometimes even seemed that no department could possibly exist without its plywood partitions and its women messengers and that only in their presence could it begin to flourish – its life seething, and its work exhaustively commented upon by its own Aunt Motya and those of neighbouring, friendly or hostile establishments. Each Aunt Motya was the jealous guardian of the prestige of her own department. Its Office Regulations were her Tables of the Law; they were subject to no criticism and had clearly been entrusted by the Lord of Hosts himself to the Commandant upon the heights of the administrative Sinai.

There were many interesting things to be seen in the plywood maze, to begin with the Cashier's office – a gloomy little cell with a crooked little window cut in the partition.

Written on it in blue pencil were the words: 'Comrades! write the amount in words and don't trouble the cashier to cut the money. Cut yourselves! (*sic*) – Ref. Order 1807.'

The mysterious and rather frightening words, 'Cut yourselves', had a simple explanation: the cashier was handed the money in large sheets which he had to waste time cutting up into separate notes. Tired of this, he took to paying the wages in uncut sheets.

The sheets varied in value according to the denomination of the notes. Thousand-rouble notes, for instance, were printed twenty to a sheet, so the sheet was worth twenty thousand, while ten-rouble notes were in sets of sixties, so the sheet was worth six hundred.

But sometimes the cashier couldn't pay in whole sheets. He had to cut the right amount with a pair of scissors.

This he put up with – it didn't take long anyway. It was only when some arrogant member of the staff refused to accept whole sheets and insisted on being paid in ready-cut notes that a row broke out.

On such occasions, the peppery old cashier slammed his little window and shouted:

'Think your hands will drop off if you cut the money? If you don't want to do it yourself, give it to the kids. Let them have a bit of fun.'

Slamming the window was a forbidden but powerful device of psychological warfare. I had experienced it myself and knew that, faced with a slammed cash-desk window, every employee panicked – especially those with many children, and alcoholics. Unaccountably, each felt sure that the window would never open again, that all the money had gone, that there was no money in the world and would never be again.

Even the most intractable claimant gave in and apologised. Then the cashier would open his window, give him a long, sad look over his spectacles and shake his head.

'Shame on you, young man. You're good at making rows, but a little thing like cutting the money yourself and saving trouble for the finance department – that's beyond you. Write the amount here, after the red asterisk.'

To enlighten the staff on currency matters, the cashier pasted up on the partition near the cash-desk a set of all the Soviet notes in circulation and, next to it, a set of those which were no longer valid.

The two sets made up a unique collection, and the only reason it wasn't stolen was that he had stuck it on with carpenter's glue so that it was impossible to strip off. Even so, the day after it was put up, Karpenko found evidence of an attempt on it: someone had started cutting the plywood with a fretsaw.

Most of the notes in those days had nicknames. Thousand-rouble notes were 'bits', millions were 'lemons', while a milliard bore the resounding name of 'lemonard'. The smaller denominations also had found unexpected names, the most endearing being kept for the small change of paper thirties and fifties.

Some of those no longer current were quite fantastic. There were the hundred roubles printed on the backs of playing cards, issued by some god-forsaken town in the Ukraine. There were Odessa notes with views of the stock exchange, there were White-Guard 'bells' and 'caps', Ukrainian 'silver roubles', hundred-rouble 'omlettes' and 'steps', and a host of other 'currency' backed by the dubious assets of various towns, from Kryzhopol to Sosnitza and from Shpola to Glukhov.

The wall beside the cash desk was colourful. As soon as he was paid his money, nearly every employee went through the same drill: he pressed the sheets against the plywood, covered them with paper and rubbed hard to get rid of the sticky surplus of printer's ink.

By the end of pay day, every surface was tacky, and our hands, desks, papers and books were covered with serial numbers and signatures of the People's Commissar of Finance.

3
Barley Gruel

The hundreds and thousands of roubles we received as so-called wages all went for mid-day meals at the neighbouring public canteen. There, day in day out, we consumed a couple of spoonfuls of barley gruel flavoured with a green, vaseline-like substance. Torelli assured us it was rifle grease.

Apart from this, we fed on scorched bread and shell fish.

The bread had one remarkable property: the crust was quite separate from the loaf. They might have been two distinct geological strata. The space between them was filled with a cloudy, sour-tasting liquid, a kind of bitter bread-juice.

Some people liked it. They sucked the juice and said that it cured swellings of the joints.

The swellings were the result of malnutrition and cold. You couldn't touch them without feeling sharp and prolonged pain, and they burst open and bled every time you tried to wash your hands. In cold weather, they ached and when it was warm they itched unbearably.

I drank bread juice and can certify that it did nothing for my swollen joints, but it did give me acute pains in the stomach.

We boiled the shellfish with salt. They tasted strongly of fish glue.

We had to gather the shellfish ourselves at Langeron, prising them from the off-shore rocks with knives; of course we could do this only in calm, warm weather. So the shellfish were strictly summer fare.

Years of Hope

We awaited summer impatiently. In summer I went fishing for goby-fish and *sultanka*. On the wide moles of the port, vegetable gardens, surrounded by fences made of rusty pipes and torn-up sheets of iron, were turning green. The leaves of the tomato plants gave off a wonderful smell, promising an early harvest of 'reddies' (as tomatoes were called in Odessa). The spectre of hunger faded for a while, but it was still there. It lay in wait for us, and we knew that at the slightest oversight on our part it would be back, and more menacing than before.

I felt I was the luckiest of men when I managed to get a few tablets of saccharine. It sweetened my beetroot tea, and as I drank it with a burnt crust of bread I felt new strength pouring into my veins.

All our money went on barley gruel and on water – a bucket cost 500 roubles. Not a penny was left, even for matches or firewood. Acacia wood the colour of sulphur was still on the market, but sold only in chips and by weight.

So we had to steal wood. I admit it without shame, if only because it was a dangerous business and the risk was sometimes deadly.

I need hardly say that we would much have preferred to feed our faithful *bourzhouika* on paper and newsprint. But old newspapers had to be stolen too.

Morally, there was little to choose between stealing papers and stealing logs, but in practice it made a great difference. Newsprint gave a fleeting hint of warmth and left the yard strewn with burnt paper and yellow ash, which brought upon us the admonitions of the unfrocked Prosvirnyak.

We stole wood mainly in Arcadia. It was the nearest residential suburb by the sea.

With the coming of summer, Arcadia made me think of the ruins of Roman villas – the Borghese, Aldobrandini or Conti. Dying ivy twined round the cracked pillars with their chipped plaster. The plaster was chipped off on purpose to make sure that the pillars were made of brick and could not be used as fuel.

Lizards sunned themselves in the glassless windows, where

golden broom flowered, clinging to broken stone windowsills. Swallows nested in the pilasters. Dusty thistles grew and multiplied in the loggias, as in enormous stone bowls.

Ants made Appian Ways on the marble slabs. Like the Coliseum with its crumbling south wall, the concrete pool had a crumbling rim on the side facing the south and the sea, while the bottom was overgrown with dry grass and immortelles.

These ruins were only about two years old but they already had an air of antiquity, and it overlaid the colours of deserted Arcadia with the dusty bronze patina of Ellas or Pergamon.

This was in summer. But in winter, when we went out at night and in bad weather, the ruins loomed ominously black. The January north wind howled in them and peppered us with small-shot of dry snow. Then it was impossible to imagine that the summer sun would one day rise over the ruins, and the softest of breezes whisper in the leaves of the surviving century-old trees.

That winter Yasha and I stole timber only three times, but we were very successful. Twice we brought back a floorboard each, and once we even got away with a door-frame.

The wood lasted us all through the winter, but only because Yasha had discovered a remarkable method of instantly bringing the *bourzhouika* to white heat and the kettle to the boil. The secret was to stoke it with splinters as thin as straw. This produced a violent though short-lived flame, and used up hardly any fuel.

I well remember our nocturnal forays for wood. First we went on a daylight reconnaissance in search of a villa where not all the timber had already been stolen. During the walk, Yasha would as usual conduct a passionate argument about the authorship of Shakespeare's plays or the economic consequences of the Treaty of Versailles.

After the reconnaissance came the main expedition. We set out before dark, following the shore where in winter it was unlikely that anyone would see us. Under our coats we carried a small hunter's axe and a brace, both belonging to Prosvirnyak. In return for this we gave him kindling for his samovar. The firewood we shared only with Torelli. His invalid sister, bedridden and unable to move, needed constant warmth.

Near Arcadia, in a derelict cabin where in prehistoric times fruit-juice and soda water were sold, we waited for nightfall.

When it was dark, we made our way to the *dacha* we had selected. We went cautiously, stopping every few minutes to listen. At the slightest sound, we hid behind the nearest wall.

It was not policemen we were afraid of. There were none in Arcadia. Who would think of guarding ruins, gardens with bare branches whistling in the wind, or the bleak shore enveloped in the gloom of a stormy night? It was not the police we were avoiding but the petty thieves, the greedy pedlars who stole timber to sell it. The markets were swarming with them.

We bumped into them the very first night, and narrowly escaped being shot with a sawn-off rifle, while the abuse showered on us made our blood run cold.

Taking up the floorboards was the hardest part of the job. It was vital to make no sound, but the rusty nails invariably squeaked. We finished up with bleeding hands, torn nails and knees shaking with strain.

The boards were incredibly heavy, as though made of cast iron. With the greatest difficulty, exhausted and staggering, we carried them to the lodge. I stoked the *bourzhouika,* while Yasha collapsed on his bed – a worn mattress on the bare floor – cursing himself, the *bourzhouika*, Odessa, the Entente and the world at large and swearing that never again would he steal wood, no, not for anything.

I wasn't feeling too cheerful either. I felt we were on a slippery path and if we didn't look out would turn into common timber thieves. But the delights of hot tea were such that we there and then forgot our pitiful attacks of conscience. After tea, Yasha went to sleep, while I lay on the Professor's hard sofa and listened for a long time to the noises of the night.

4
Blockade

Memory plays many unaccountable tricks on us.

Our recollection of great events can be as hazy as that of a grey uneventful day.

I have tried to avoid this danger in my writing, but I am not sure of having been completely successful. The image we retain of a period can be subjective even though it seems to us objective and accurate. How otherwise account for the fact that, amidst all the resounding and amazing events of the time, our life in Odessa at the end of 1920 and in 1921 seems to me in retrospect a relatively peaceful interlude?

Odessa was deserted. Many workers had left with the first Red Army units – supply divisions and sailors' detachments – before the arrival of Denikin and the Interventionists.[7] Many other people had fled to the country, to escape hunger and mobilisation by the Whites.

The city had hardly any important industries. The largest were the jute and canning factories and the dry docks. The town was dominated by the port and its poor – dockhands, tramps and layabouts – while the stubborn and resourceful middle class had dug in on the outskirts of the city.

During the Intervention, the workers who had stayed in Odessa gave every assistance to the Bolshevik underground.

The Bolsheviks were in hiding in the quarries, right inside the town. In spite of arrests and shootings, their daring was such that, even during the joint French and Denikin occupation, they held a

regional Bolshevik conference, regularly published an underground paper, *Communist*, distributed leaflets, helped the printers
and the telegraph and tramway workers who were on strike, blew
up a train carrying supplies for the Interventionists, and ended by
forming a war-revolutionary committee which provisionally took
over the administration when the Soviet troops occupied
Odessa.

Shortly before this, when already there was fighting in the
suburbs, nine young underground Bolsheviks were caught by
Denikin's counter-intelligence and shot after being horribly
tortured. The account of these mediaeval tortures shook even the
hardened population of Odessa.

I remember the stories about Ida Krasnoshchekina who bore the
brunt of the fury of the Whites and showed unbelievable firmness
and courage.

Before their death the prisoners wrote, in a letter to their free
comrades: 'We are dying but we have triumphed.' These simple
and moving words hold all the passion and boundless faith in
victory which have become the hallmark of young revolutionaries.

By the end of Denikin's second occupation, there were even
fewer workers left in the city. Nearly all the factories had shut
down. The port was derelict. Life was at a standstill. Only black-
marketeering raged like a bush fire.

In addition there was a wide rift in outlook between those who
came from the north, and were living a third year of the revolution, and the Odessans for whom the revolution was only a few
months old.

I, too, experienced not one but three October Revolutions – in
1917 in Moscow, in 1918 in Kiev and in 1920 in Odessa.

The revolution not only brought with it to Odessa the new
political and social structure developed in the north, it also brought
new men, trained by the revolution and alien to the mentality and
practical experience of the average Odessan.

Resolute and ruthless men appeared (all referred to, indis-
criminately, as 'Commissars') who knew exactly what to do to

ensure the triumph of the revolutionary outlook in the minds of the mixed southern population, impulsive and prone to anarchical acts.

One reason for the seeming quiet of our life was the blockade which lasted through the winter of 1920 and all through 1921. For months the sea lay flat and lifeless, without a trace of smoke from a ship's funnel. At the same time, blocked railways, blown-up bridges, bandit gangs and the 'wild lands'[8] which knew no law, cut Odessa off from the north.

All this accounts for the singularity of Odessa's way of life at that time.

I often woke up on the Professor's couch and listened to the night. This had become my favourite hobby.

The night gradually filled with silence. I listened to its approach, and the occasional faint sound of distant gunfire. It came from the French gunboat *La Scarpe* which regularly shelled Ochakov by night.

The heavy silence and the echoing shots were signs of the blockade. Until then I had only read the word in history books and in adventure stories as old as green oxide on bronze. Still, I had a fairly clear image of it.

'Blockade' meant an empty sea swept by fast patrol ships; naval guns trained on suburban vegetable gardens; extinct lighthouses; a blown-up transport ship showing the tip of its mast at the harbour entrance; a distant searchlight probing the milky way; and a feeling of lightness brought on by hunger.

If these were signs of blockade, the blockade of Odessa ran true to type. They all appeared in our daily life, though sometimes fantasy and reality were so mixed up that it was hard to tell one from the other.

In spite of hunger, the cold, damp lodge, the devastation and the loneliness (in spring Yasha went to live in town and I was left on my own) I was sometimes unaccountably filled with elation. I ascribed this to my youth; not that I was so young – I would soon be getting on for thirty – but I felt as though I were eighteen. I was against everything adult, positive and sensible – against it, though sometimes also scared of it like a schoolboy.

I reacted in this childish way to everything in Odessa, even to the long spring and summer of the blockade.

'Blockade' meant an empty sea – and the sea was empty, and I liked it.

It was as empty as in the days before man had even learned to build a raft. You could watch it for weeks and months on end from the Boulevard, and never see anything except the sun flashing on the ripples.

Occasionally a squadron of strange ships appeared on the horizon, advancing haughtily under taut white sails, but as they drew nearer they turned into menacing, snow-covered mountains that suddenly thundered and flashed lightning at the darkened waves.

The sea responded to the voices of the clouds, turning a single clap of thunder into a multitude of reverberating peals that shook the watery expanse in all directions.

Every time I had a day off I went to the country, usually to the far end of Great Fountain.

Spring had come. In the steppe along the sea, it was more touching than in places rich in vegetation – perhaps because here you noticed every separate flower that struggled from under the rusty rails of the disused tramline, and every butterfly that fluttered, drying its wings, in a stream of warm sea air.

That warm air rose in steady, powerful exhalations from the foot of the steep red cliffs, from the beaches which the war had cluttered up with the wreckage of steamers and sailing boats. It seemed even to come from the hull of the minesweeper *Xanthe*. Wrecked off the shore of Great Fountain, she had wedged herself into the rocks and no one had so much as tried to re-float her.

Water gurgled, flowing in and out of her cabins and holds, and crabs climbed confidently up her sides, to warm themselves on the riveted metal plates of her deck.

And still the sea remained a desert, and I think we would not have been surprised to catch sight of coloured Phoenician sails or of bronze prows of Greek triremes, long since vanished from the world.

The idea of ancient times goes with that of wilderness. There were, after all, very few people in the world in the days of the triremes, so the continents and seas were largely deserts.

But the reason why the Black Sea was a desert was partly the blockade, and partly that, when the Whites had fled from Odessa, they had taken with them the whole of the so-called merchant fleet – all the tugs, barges, cutters and passenger and cargo ships belonging to the Volunteer Navy, the Black Sea–Danube Company and the ROPIT (Russian Passenger and Cargo Line).

The fleet was taken to various Mediterranean ports where the White Command was selling it to foreign companies.

The Whites had taken privately owned ships as well, even the junk that had belonged to the notorious ship-owner Shay Kropotsky. Shay had been the laughing stock of all seafaring Odessa. His meanness and his double dealing were a legend. Not even a cab-driver would give him credit. Only down-and-outs agreed to serve on his ships, and they had literally to shake him for their pay – take him by the scruff of the neck and shake him.

Shay had owned the antedeluvian paddle-steamer *Turgenev* which plied between Odessa and Ackerman and which Katayev[9] described in his *White Sail* – though some native Odessans dispute this and assert that the *Turgenev* belonged to the firm of Mishures and Sons.

Lost in the ships' graveyard among the rubbish dumps at the back of the oil port were a few old wrecks waiting to be broken up, among them rusted through and through, the *Dimitry*, which had also belonged to Shay. That ship was very nearly to cost me my life.

The harbour was as calm as a lagoon. Its proper function lost, it had become a breeding pool for bullheads and mackerel, and the favourite resort of aged fishermen.

Oats (from spilled grain) and sweet-smelling yellow camomile grew on the breakwaters. The mooring posts were so thick with rust that you could scarcely see the name of the manufacturers – Bellino-Fenderikh – engraved on the metal.

The harbour watchmen grew vegetables on the wide piers.

Of all the countless vegetable plots I have seen, these were the most attractive. Amidst the jungle of tomato plants each owner placed a packing case to serve as a seat. There you could sit and smoke and listen to conversation of every sort.

Every plot had its scarecrow to keep away the sparrows. They were made to look like tramps in sailors' vests and bell-bottoms made of sacking. A battered bowler hat or a child's quilted bonnet covered the rag-doll head. The bowler, set at a rakish angle, gave the scarecrow a shameless appearance, as though at any moment it might break into a *danse macabre* or a can-can.

The one that was most admired stood on watchman Dukonin's plot on Quarantine Pier. It represented a drunken skipper with a bottle of vodka in his hand and was known as 'Dukonin's George'. Instead of vodka the bottle was full of sea-water but the habitués of the port were none the less delighted with George and always gave a noisy welcome to his owner.

There were other anti-sparrow devices: little windmills with ply-wood sails that drummed on splinters of glass hanging on twine – this made a pleasant melodious tinkle which the sparrows could not abide; and coloured rags that fluttered from bamboo sticks, furling and unfurling in the wind.

All these things, including scarcerows in the port, were secondary signs of the blockade, which, for the time being, operated fairly peacefully (even the *La Scarpe* had moved away from the shore at the beginning of summer) and therefore encouraged the Odessans' peaceful and even idyllic pursuits.

The Polish war[10] hadn't reached Odessa. All was quiet. Only rarely did the roar of gunfire come from the sea, always from the side of Ochakov and the Kinburn Spit. This happened when Vrangel's cruiser, *Kagul*, came from the Crimea and shelled the coast at random. Our shore batteries drove it off and it turned readily back with an air of mission accomplished – belching smoke, rolling mountains of shining spray, and flying a faded St Andrew's flag from its gaff.

Another sign of the blockade was the fact that a tiny piece of hard maize-bread and ten apricots were considered a sufficient diet.

Working at Oprodkomgub, we knew the superhuman effort needed to supply the town at all; it was like feeding its thousands on the five loaves of the Gospel parable.

Bread was issued against ration cards – or, as they were called, 'by letters'. The cards were marked with all the letters of the alphabet from A to Z, each denoting the category to which the consumer belonged. The As got most, the Zs about enough to feed a canary. I belonged to category K.

I liked standing in the long queues. The life of a queue, though brief, was interesting. It lived on fantastic rumours, anecdotes, sudden panics, arguments and jokes about some bit of worldly wisdom someone had dropped, and of course on rows. The rows blew up as suddenly as rockets, but took a long time to die down, like dust after an explosion.

Fights were rare and took the harmless form of people pushing each other in the chest with the flat of the hand.

Once I witnessed a scene of which the verbal economy and effective pantomime deeply impressed me.

Standing in the queue was a short, old, Jewish gentleman in a dusty bowler and a worn black coat reaching to his ankles. Smiling and nodding benevolently, he observed the queue through unusually thick spectacles. Now and then he took out of his pocket a small black book with the Star of David embroidered in gold on the cover, read a page or two and returned the book to his pocket.

He must surely be a scholar, I thought, perhaps even a *tsaddic*,[11] an old philosopher from Portofrank Street, his tranquil spirit unshaken, his kindliness unchilled and the smile in his blue, child-like eyes undimmed by the misfortunes of a lifetime.

Watching the queue from the side was a young man with an impudent air, a black skull-cap, and down-at-heel but shiny, canary-coloured shoes.

Leather shoes were a great rarity. People went about in clogs. The town echoed to their drumming. In the morning, when everyone was hurrying to work, if you shut your eyes you could imagine that the entire population of Odessa was dancing to casta-nets. So the queue watched the impudent young man's canary-coloured shoes with deep envy and admiring looks and sighs.

The young man was wondering how to jump the queue without causing a fuss and a row. He saw the old gentleman with the book, and naturally took him for the very embodiment of mildness and non-resistance to evil. Making up his mind, he skilfully inserted his shoulder between him and his neighbour in the queue and, pushing the old man, muttered casually:

'Excuse me.'

Still with the same smile, the old man bent his sharp little elbow, drew it back, took aim and, dealing the young man a swift and forceful blow in the chest, right under the heart, said politely:

'Not at all. Excuse *me*.'

The young man grunted and flew back, hitting an acacia tree. His cap fell off his head. He picked it up and walked away without looking back. Only at the corner did he turn and shake his fist at the old man, whimpering

'Jailbird! Bandit!'

The queue was silent – its collective thought had not had time to crystallise and find expression – while the old man took his book out of his pocket and immersed himself in it, evidently searching for some kernel of truth which he would later discuss with his cronies in the quiet of Portofrank Street.

If the weeks and months of the blockade could seem peaceful and untroubled to a part of the population, this was only because it knew nothing of what was happening outside the town. In reality, the situation was grim and the new administration had need of all its resourcefulness and self-reliance to cope with the danger to the city.

After the flight of Denikin's main army, a force of some seventy thousand of his officers and men had been left behind and were concentrated in the various German settlements – Liebenthal, Lustdorf, Marienthal – on the outskirts of the town.

Blockade

The Allies relied on them to promote an uprising in Odessa, which they on their side would then support with artillery fire from their ships.

Apart from this, there were, at a conservative estimate, some two thousand bandits, burglars, thieves, forgers, fences and other shady characters living in the suburbs of Moldavanka, Bugayevka, Slobodka-Romanovka and Inner and Outer Mills.

Their mood was uncertain. As a general rule, bandits tend to be hysterical and unstable in their attachments. No one could tell what they would do if there were an uprising.

There were very few Soviet troops in Odessa. Meanwhile an Allied squadron was already cruising offshore, having sent the Italian mine sweeper *Raccia* ahead on reconnaissance.

But an event took place which sharply changed the situation. The *Raccia* struck a mine when it was beam-on to the Great Fountain lighthouse. All we heard of it in town was the faint echo of an explosion at sea, which alarmed no one.

By order of the Provincial Committee, fishermen from Golden Shore, Great Fountain, the Kovalevsky estate and Lustdorf – all experienced and level headed men – went out in their barges, picked up the survivors and the bodies of the dead, and brought them ashore before the squadron had had time to reach the scene of the shipwreck.

The bodies of the dead were taken to Odessa, and a signal was sent to the Commander of the squadron. It informed him that the city was grieved by the disaster and wished to assume the burden of a solemn funeral for the gallant victims, and it invited him to attend the ceremony and to send sailors' units to form a guard of honour.

The admiral agreed – there was not much else he could do.

Next morning, unarmed Soviet soldiers and sailors formed up all along the way from the port to Kulikov Field where a common grave had been dug. Mourning flags hung on all the houses, and the way was strewn with flowers and branches of thuya.

A hundred thousand Odessans – almost the entire population at that time – attended the funeral.

Dock workers carried the coffins. After them came sunburnt Italian sailors, rifles pointing down.

The bands of the foreign ships played, as well as the combined Odessa band. Ours did not disgrace itself, and the heart-rending strains of Chopin's Funeral March made the sensitive Odessan women wipe away their tears with their shawls.

The bells tolled mournfully from New Athos Church. The roofs were black with watching crowds.

Speeches were made at the grave. The Italians listened and presented arms. Then the distant sound of a salvo at sea mingled with that of a volley of rifle-shots on Kulikov Field. A pyramid of flowers rose over the grave.

After the funeral the foreign sailors were given supper at the former Frankoni café. Comrade Agin dipped into the sacred food reserve for the occasion, and used up most of it.

After such a funeral, how could there be any question of bombardment or of uprising? The sailors of the foreign ships would not have stood for it. They were grateful for the honour paid their fallen comrades and for the warmth of their own reception.

The old admiral (who looked like Giuseppe Verdi) decided that the game was up and ordered the squadron back to Constantinople. It vanished into the gloom of the evening, leaving Denikin's officers to their fate.

By allowing armed foreign sailors into the town, the Provincial Committee had taken a huge risk, but it was an honourable one, and the funeral proved a bloodless victory over the Interventionists.

Soon afterwards, the blockade was lifted, and the first barge-loads of apricots sailed into the port from Kherson.

Then, on a cloudless morning, two Turkish feluccas from Skutari, colourful as a picture, tied in at the Quarantine Pier – they were the first cargo ships to reach Odessa.

Next day the papers announced triumphantly that two feluccas had arrived from Turkey with a kilo of flints for cigarette lighters, glass beads, gilt bracelets, and a small barrel of olives.

What mattered, of course, was not the kilo of flints, but the fact that the sea was free again. This seemed to me suddenly to alter its appearance: gay under a gusty wind, it shone with such snow-white spray as I had never seen on it before.

Any day now, we would see, in the blue distance to the south-west, the mighty hulls and yellow funnels and strange flags of ocean-going craft, and would hear whistles and rumbling anchor-chains – a sound which promised those who sailed the seas a well-earned rest in a beautiful though foreign land.

5
Concatenation of Circumstances

Volodya Golovchiner was fond of reflecting on the 'cunning and unpredictable concatenations of circumstances' which rule our fate. He quoted Chekhov's *Ivanov* to prove it: 'We, human beings, live like the flowers of the field. Along comes a goat and – snip! there's no flower.'

Torelli agreed, adding that, whatever might be true in the world at large, you could never be sure of anything in Odessa. Odessa was a law unto itself. Anything might happen, even a full-scale battle over a set of kitchen chairs, as had been the case during the Intervention in 1919.

The Interventionists had divided the city into four zones – French, Greek, Petlyura's and Denikin's, each fenced off by a row of bent-wood chairs. One day, when the French sentry had left his post on urgent business, Petlyura's men pinched some of them, thereby annexing a large slice of foreign territory. When he came back the indignant sentry 'started a commotion' and began to shoot.

However this may be, the following incident proved Volodya's point: the cause was indeed a complicated and unpredictable combination (or 'concatenation,' as he insisted) of circumstances.

Early one morning in summer, when the blockade was at its height and Odessa's total isolation induced a certain recklessness in her mood, Torelli hammered on our door and shouted:

'Get up! There seems to be a new Intervention.'

I leapt out of bed. In Odessa you had to be prepared for anything. From the top of the cliffs overlooking Langeron and the port veiled in its delicate faint-blue mist, we saw what Torelli described as rosy-fingered Aurora (drifts of cloud over the sea, lit by a quiet dawn) and, on the clear waters of the harbour, two enormous, clumsy, ocean-going liners flying the French flag.

The French mine sweeper *Lieutenant Borri,* long and elegant as a fine cigar, lay beside them, a wisp of smoke over her funnel and the brasswork on her deck dazzling as the sun.

We rushed down to the port, but were not allowed in. It was cordoned off by units of sailors and Red Army men.

The two French transport ships were slowly moving towards their berths. We heard that the commander of the minesweeper was the well-known French writer Claude Farrère, author of *Opium Dreams.*

This was sufficiently interesting in itself. Still more interesting was the disembarkation which followed.

Calmly walking down the gangways of the troopship were not Zouaves, not coffee-coloured Senegalese, not even men of the Foreign Legion, but Russian soldiers, unarmed and in brand new khaki uniforms, indistinguishable from those of the old Tsarist army except for the addition of squeaky polished leggings of brown leather.

The men formed up on the quay and were marched off to barracks by Soviet commanders.

An hour later we knew all about it. 'All' was the fact that, during the War, Nicolas II had sent an infantry corps, known as the Russian Expeditionary Force, to France. It sailed from Vladivostock, landed in Marseilles and marched through Paris under the eyes of delighted Frenchwomen who showered the men with flowers.

President Poincaré took the parade at the Arc de Triomphe, where they marched past to the rousing strains of '*Chubariki-chubchiki,* trouble isn't grief.'

The French Command was not so keen to share the fruits of victory with Russian bears as to hurry them off to the front; all the same about five thousand of our men were killed in battles with the Germans on French soil.

Then came the revolution and the Russians refused to continue to fight. They were sent to the rear and interned in prisoner-of-war camps. There they remained for several years, although they kept demanding repatriation and even mutinied from time to time, causing considerable trouble to the French authorities.

In the end, the French decided to get rid of them, put them on troopships and, by agreement with our government, sent them under convoy to Odessa.

All Odessa flocked to the port to welcome the Russian soldiers. They were hugged, kissed and presented with flowers.

Then a mysterious incident occurred.

The disembarkation over, the ships left their moorings and were sailing past the Vorontsov lighthouse into the roadstead when, from our Black Sea Street, a volley thundered, and shells exploded across their bows.

The two transport ships stopped their engines while the minesweeper turned broadside-on to the port, and a dazzling violet light flashed on and off from its conning tower, signalling Odessa.

Meanwhile guns were being mounted on the Promenade. Sailors with Mausers at their belts worked in grim and concentrated silence.

All Odessa learned that, hidden in their holds, the troopships carried a large cargo of arms and even some light tanks.

The French had meant to kill two birds with one stone: rid themselves of the Russian revolutionaries, then call on the Crimea on their way to Constantinople and unload the arms for Vrangel.[12]

The Odessa authorities had found this out from the men of the Expeditionary Force and asked Moscow by radio for instructions.

The order came to detain the ships and demand that the arms be landed in Odessa.

The French refused. It was said in Odessa that the whole dirty business had been thought up by General d'Anselme; even the Whites, his allies, thought him stupid as a donkey and as mean as Plyushhkin.[13]

Two days passed. All Odessa crowded on to the beaches,

waiting to see what would happen. The French were adamant and kept up steam; their funnels never stopped puffing.

They were evidently looking for some dignified way out, but finally could think of nothing better than brute force.

A strong squadron of French warships was despatched from Constantinople. Its commander signalled grimly that he would shell the coast and raze Odessa to the ground unless the ships were released.

I still remember our bitter disappointment when, to save Odessa, Moscow advised the release of the ships. We were not strong enough at sea then to take on a whole French squadron.

The day the ships left, I went to Fountain where the cliffs looked out on to the open sea. A thick pall of smoke shrouded the horizon. The French squadron was approaching. It stopped a few miles away and waited for its troopships.

The troopships were sailing full steam ahead. Swooping after them and darting from ship to ship came the minesweeper *Lieutenant Borri*. The sight must have been too much for one of our shore batteries which fired a useless salvo in their wake.

I felt cruelly hurt for France and for the French, hurt for the whole of their great culture, for Diderot and Voltaire, Hugo and Stendhal, for Zola and Corot, for Pasteur and Delacroix, for all the great Frenchmen whom none of us distinguished from Russians. They were as close to us as Pushkin, Tolstoy and Chekhov. They would have felt bitterly ashamed of France's political confidence-tricksters and their representative, General d'Anselme. I could imagine how coldly and contemptuously Hugo or Stendhal would have had the General shot for cowardice and knavery.

6

Day of Peaceful Uprising

We had been without electricity for so long that we were beginning to forget it had ever existed. Bulbs were black with dirt, and if you turned a switch by mistake it squeaked with rust.

Only Volodya was delighted. With the air of making a discovery, he announced: 'Every epoch has its distinctive style. Ours is that of a new pastoral age. Think of it – no electricity. Nettles growing on the tramlines. Potatoes flowering in the squares. We wear Greek buskins on our feet and drink fresh water instead of vodka. What could be nicer? It's the dawn of the golden age.'

One day I wasn't feeling well and stayed in bed instead of going to Oprodkomgub. It was late in spring. The chestnuts were in flower and in the evening a mist-wrapped moon rose over the sea.

I lit the oil lamp and was quietly reading the tenth volume of Brockhaus and Efron's Encyclopaedia when something strange and disturbing happened – the filament in the bulb of the ceiling lamp turned yellow and began to glow, though without reaching anything like a state of full incandescence. The room filled with an unpleasant, pallid light that made it look like a morgue.

I watched, hypnotised, wondering why the light was so dim. Obviously the feeble current was dragging itself along rusty wires, struggling with ancient connections and dusty knots of insulating tape and getting stuck in the meters choked with cobwebs.

Just as I thought the light was growing brighter, it faded almost to vanishing point. All the same, there was enough of it to light up the oak book-cases and sombre rows of books.

Day of Peaceful Uprising

It struck me that there was something sinister about the light suddenly coming on. It was an omen, a warning. I was not alone in this. Odessa secretly panicked. The light meant trouble. What kind of trouble?

Torelli gave me a hint. He knocked and came in, pale, wild eyed, a woman's brand-new coat with a monkey collar over his arm.

'Could I possibly ask you to hang it up in your cupboard?' he asked hurriedly. 'Just for a few days. It's my sister's.'

I was taken aback but I took the coat and hung it up. It was a light spring coat and smelt faintly of scent. Clearly, Torelli's sister Rachel, still a pretty girl with freckles on her face, had never once worn it since her illness.

'What's the matter?' I asked Torelli.

'It's a matter of logic.' He gave an artificial laugh and rubbed his hands. 'You know as well as I do that the power station has enough coal-dust for three nights. Yet they've started it up. That means that before the three nights are out, something is going to happen. Something that requires electric light.'

'But what could happen?'

'How do I know?' He shrugged. 'St Bartholomew's Night? Massacre of the Innocents? Rape of the Sabines? The last days of Pompeii? You can take your choice. Good night.'

He went, leaving me to rack my brains.

I couldn't think of anything, so I went back to bed. I tried to switch out the light – the switch squeaked but the light stayed on. I waggled the switch up and down. It squeaked loud and angrily but the light didn't even blink. I climbed up on a chair and tried to unscrew the bulb, but it had soldered itself to the socket.

I got into bed, leaving the windows open. The drowsy, rhythmic sound of the waves lulled me to sleep.

I awoke at dawn. Dew was gathering on the branches of the thuya outside my window. The garden was deserted and still. But in the near corner, where an old barrel of lime had always stood, there was a large, dark, shapeless object, rather like a hayrick.

I looked hard at it. Somehow it was frightening. Pulling myself together, I climbed through the window into the garden and went up to it. It was a heap of old but expensive coats. There was skunk with a beaver collar, a woman's astrakhan coat, two old-fashioned black spring coats and an astrakhan jacket.

Underneath the layers of fur I found a low stool, upholstered in damask, with curly gilt legs. I had seen one like it on the stage, under the feet of the old Countess in *The Queen of Spades*.

I pulled it out and tried to lift it to have a closer look, but soon gave up – it seemed to be filled with lead.

I kicked it and heard something tinkle inside, under the elegant Louis XIV upholstery. The mystery deepened. I meant to solve it, but I first ran out to the nearest shop to buy bread. The shop stayed open only two hours – I was afraid of being late.

Coming back, I found that the pile in the corner of the garden had been camouflaged with straw and fallen leaves, so neatly that no one would have guessed there was anything there.

I dislike mysteries. Knowing that Prosvirnyak had the key of the door from the yard into the garden, I went to ask him what was going on.

Prosvirnyak was our political barometer. If he looked away when he met us, pretended not to hear, interrupted us by shouting at his cook, a former nun, 'Don't put too much oil in, Neonilla,' it meant that the regime in Odessa had suffered a setback, however slight.

But if he went out of his way to be amiable, laughing an affected, deep laugh and stroking his beard with both hands, we knew that the regime stood firm.

That day he was polite but livid.

'You of all people,' he said with quiet emphasis, 'as a civil servant with however limited a responsibility for the actions of your masters, should know that a Day of Peaceful Uprising has been proclaimed in Odessa. According to the authorities, the Day is to last three days.'

'I haven't heard,' I said. 'I haven't been to town yet. What is this Peaceful Uprising?'

He spread a grey sheet of paper in front of me. His hands were shaking. 'I tore this down with my own hands from the wall of my own house at eleven o'clock last night.'

I read the order signed by the Odessa Provincial Committee. It said that, as a means of expropriating the possessing classes, whose wealth was now the property of the people, a Day of Peaceful Uprising was proclaimed. All citizens without exception were to hand over their surplus food and belongings, and keep only the listed essentials.

I read the list. It said: 'To be left for the citizen's private use, one suit of outer clothing, one set of underwear, one pair of shoes (not boots), one headgear,' and so on down to 'one fork, knife, soup-spoon, mug, cooking utensils (only those essential), and one hundred grams of sugar.

'In the event of gold, valuables, foreign currency, or luxury or black-market goods being found, those who concealed them will be brought to trial for treason and counter-revolution.'

'Swine,' said Prosvirnyak, making me start. I had never before heard a coarse word from his honeyed lips.

'And now,' I said, 'will you kindly remove your stuff from under my windows and hide it elsewhere. As you may appreciate, I don't want to be shot because of your moth-eaten coats and your foot-stools stuffed with gold.'

'You are very much mistaken,' he said gently, pressing his hand to his breast. 'You have no reason to be angry. Two of the coats are mine, but the footstool belongs to General Rennenkampf's sister-in-law. I couldn't refuse, especially as she had seen me hiding my own stuff. Put yourself in my shoes. I'll take it all away as soon as it's dark.'

'Right,' I agreed. 'But mind, not later than tonight.'

Forgetting, apparently, that he was unfrocked, Prosvirnyak raised his arms to heaven and proclaimed in an affectedly inspired voice, as though from a pulpit (while his eyes flashed angrily): 'These are evil times indeed! Truly there are no bounds to human wickedness and the wiles of Satan.'

Dropping his arms, he went on in his ordinary voice:

'You I respect, but that Comrade Gavarsaki – the electrician, the tenant in Flat 3 – he worries me terribly. He's buying up explosives. One of these days, they'll pick him up and us as well and shoot the lot of us. I'll stake my life on it. Beware of him. Be careful he doesn't bury his infernal fireworks in the garden. The coats are nothing. At the worst, the "comrades" will take them. I'm prepared for anything.'

I went away convinced that he had not the slightest intention of removing his belongings, and indeed, when I came back with Yasha from the office, the pile had stretched from one end of the garden wall to the other. All the things were covered up with straw as carefully as the first lot which, by comparison, seemed to me quite small.

Dozing on a kitchen chair beside them was an imposing old gentleman with white side-whiskers. There was such a period air about him that you might have thought a story by Goncharov or Ostrovsky was being filmed in the garden.

'You haven't moved your things, of course,' I said to Prosvirnyak. 'But be that between you and your conscience. Who is the character in the garden?'

'The watchman,' he said mysteriously. 'Between ourselves, people have brought their things from all over Black Sea Street – it's such a secluded place here. They're afraid of two things, naturally. On the one hand, the authorities may come and take everything, and on the other there are the bandits – you never know when they will strike. So we decided to keep watch in turn. Comrade Gavarsaki tried to get in with his fireworks, but I didn't let him.'

'What fireworks?'

'A liquid of some sort. In two-gallon carboys. He's a fool that Gavarsaki.'

'Hm . . . yes,' said Yasha, having learned what was going on in the house and garden. 'It's going to end in a God-awful mess, I can tell you here and now.'

Going to the office that morning, I had been struck by the unusual amount of traffic in town – especially the number of prams, push-carts and anything on wheels suitable for the transport of small objects; there were even bicycles loaded like mules and low wooden platforms on castors. The prams were mostly ramshackle and held together with string.

All this stream of baby carriages rolled towards the Greek market; so did the briskly rattling hand-carts pushed from behind. People were hurrying in the same direction, panting under the weight of parcels and suitcases, or dragging lamps and sewing machines, tailor's dummies and dentists' chairs.

This great migration was taking place in complete silence. Even the children in the prams uttered no sound. Not a squeak nor a howl – well wrapped up and sheltered by curtains and hoods, they were all fast asleep. And they must all have been future giants, judging by the way the prams sagged under their weight.

This went on all day. The staff of Oprodkomgub watched from the windows. The slightest hold-up in the traffic made the watchers uneasy. Leaning out, they called in worried voices:

'What's the matter? Won't they let you through? Try Perekop. They'll leave that to the last.'

'No, they're not stopping us,' the people in the street called back reluctantly. 'It's just a pram that's broken down. It's holding us all up.'

'What's in it?' The watchers asked with lively interest.

'Tins of halva! About two hundred pounds of it. A whole consignment.'

Torelli explained it all to me the moment I got to the office. The night before, the search parties had gone through the Greek market district, expropriating superfluous wealth. So now, people from other parts of the town – the Station district, for instance, where the expropriation was still to come – were moving their valuables to the Greek market for safety. If, by next day, the Station district had had its turn, prams and people would flow back, making room for those from French Boulevard.

Yasha and I couldn't sleep all night. The owners of the property hidden in the garden kept flitting about like bats, vanishing at the slightest sound as though the earth had swallowed them up.

We also stayed awake waiting for a search party to arrive at any moment – no one knew when it would be the turn of our street.

So we listened to all the strange sounds which came from outside and, to pass the time, tried to identify them.

The rustling in the main building was made up of the anxious whispers of the tenants in all the flats. Rising above it, could be heard the nagging, whining voice of Comrade Gavarsaki who had still not managed to dispose of his carboys of unidentified liquid explosive.

'It's all very well laughing,' said Yasha. 'If I were you I'd take that damned footstool out and get rid of it. Throw it over the wall into the next yard. Don't you realise you're risking your neck? How are you going to prove it's not yours?'

'All right,' I said. 'You go and do it. And you deal with that mob of owners. I don't care by now.'

Yasha snorted.

'Hi, you!' he suddenly shouted through the window at a thick shadow, which immediately disappeared in terror. 'You property owners out there! Ladies and gentlemen in waiting! Will you stop milling outside our window or not? Nobody can get a wink of sleep with all that row going on.'

An angry black tuft of hair stood up on his head. Outside, perfect silence 'reigned' as they say. I burst out laughing and hid my face in my pillow.

'What's the matter with you?' Yasha turned on me.

But just then Comrade Gavarsaki walked in through the door from the yard without knocking. He stopped on the threshold and looked at us reproachfully, arms folded on his chest.

'What do you want, young man?' Yasha asked in a tone implying 'Go to hell'.

But Gavarsaki didn't even look at him. I should explain that Gavarsaki's appearance was against him. The long face and muddy skin, the long dark nose, slightly askew, the yellow circles round the mournful eyes, the shuffling gait, the mumbling voice – all spoke of failure and querulous resignation to fate.

Day of Peaceful Uprising

For a long time Gavarsaki stood in silence, open-mouthed, his eyes slowly searching the room.

'There's a space there,' he said at last. 'Behind that door. It would take one carboy. The trouble is I've got three.'

Yasha's eyes widened with fear:

'What is he talking about? What does he want?'

'Or could I put them in your cupboard?' Gavarsaki asked calmly. 'They wouldn't harm your things. I use pure ether.'

'Ether?'

'Pure ether, I tell you. *Ether sulphuricus.* What did you think? I get three sacks of flour and a bottle of lamp-oil for every carboy. That's not to be sneezed at. Of course, if they find it they shoot you. But they'll never come to the lodge. Why should they? It's just an out-house. It's not like my room with the three carboys in the middle of it, like on a stage. It's got me worried, honestly comrades, it's a real headache.'

Yasha jumped out of bed, went up to Gavarsaki, and hissed with extraordinary venom:

'Get out! At once! Or I'll kick you through that door. Out!'

Gavarsaki scratched his head, blinked at me, asked, 'Is he always like that your friend? Sounds mental!' and reluctantly went out, closing the door carefully behind him.

Yasha locked it, blew out the wick-lamp and went back to bed, but he tossed for a long time in the dark, cursing the ill wind that had brought him to Black Sea Street.

I was dozing off when I smelt an unfamiliar, rather pungent smell. Suddenly I was floating, and my heart was gradually slowing down.

It stopped after a faint last flutter, without causing me any fear or pain, and a delightful freshness poured over me. I even laughed with pleasure.

Immediately, Yasha's voice roared as though from the centre of the earth:

'Get up! Quick! Ether!'

He jerked my arm. I tried to sit up but fell back. He seized me by the shoulders and dragged me, reeling, to the window.

'Get out into the garden,' he shouted, pushing me. 'Curse that Gavarsaki. Get out or we're finished! Hurry! Come on!'

I leaned with difficulty through the window. Someone from outside pulled me clear and picked me up. It was Torelli. Yasha climbed out after me. A strong, sharp smell filled the lodge.

'For God's sake,' Prosvirnyak shouted brokenly, 'don't smoke, don't strike a match. I beg of you! Or the building will go up. And don't go near the sewage pipe, you'll be killed.'

I came to. It was dawn. The garden was full of terrified lodgers, huddling against the walls. Torelli's sister lay on a blanket under the acacia tree.

'What has happened?' I asked. 'Has there been a search?'

'Nothing like that,' Torelli answered with forced heartiness. 'The Lord chose to work a miracle.'

At this, all the tenants began to laugh. The women rocked with laughter, covering their mouths with their shawls, the men shook silently, Torelli squealed and Prosvirnyak rumbled, stroking his beard. Even Yasha spluttered and choked.

I felt terrified.

'Stop!' I shouted. 'Tell me what's happened.'

It appeared that at two in the morning a search party had knocked up the house next door. Driven mad with terror, Gavarsaki rushed into the lavatory with his carboys, poured the ether down the drain, and immediately vanished without trace.

The fumes filled the building, poured along the pipes into the lodge and the next house, and seeped through flanges and man-holes, out into the street and the other yards.

Everyone in our building and the next had got out safely. Torelli's sister was carried out just in time. Driven back by the fumes and the fear of being poisoned, the search party withdrew to the far end of the street and, after searching a few houses, went off at first light, swearing to find Gavarsaki even at the bottom of the sea, and knock his head off.

That day the belongings left in our garden went back to their owners, disappearing quickly and without fuss. Prosvirnyak swept the garden, a shower of rain laid the dust and washed away all trace of the nocturnal commotion; and once again the blue seaside silence enveloped the lodge, never again to leave it.

Yasha moved back to town. Volodya Golovchiner moved into the lodge in his place.

The flats still smelt of ether. Gavarsaki turned up at the end of a week, safe, but exhausted and batty.

And although he had saved them from a house search, the tenants turned on him to a man. Never a day passed without some new comic story being spread about him.

Gavarsaki scratched his head and looked in vain for a drop of sympathy. They had none to give him. Only Volodya had the patience to listen to him, and even he, after Gavarsaki had gone, shook his head and sighed:

'What can you do with a chap like that!'

7
The Austrian Beach

Quarantine Wharf was sheltered from the sea by a high wall of concrete blocks. At its far end, it widened into the pier.

Violent winter storms had broken a wide gap in the wall and formed a small sandy beach on the side facing the sea. The first to use it had been Austrian soldiers during the Intervention, so this warm, cosy, secluded beach was known as 'Austria'.

It was further away from town than the wide beach of Langeron Bay, so those who went were mostly people fond of solitude – and perhaps also of the kind of old-fashioned marine views you hardly ever see except in old illustrated magazines. For to get to it, you had to walk right across the port, past half-buried, round dismantled mines, yellow and red buoys, stone steps leading to the water, signal-masts, old barges, coils of rotten rope and finally, a mysterious little house with a white turret and rusted balcony, standing on the breakwater. It had no windows on the first floor which made it look rather like a fort or a blockhouse.

The roof was of orange tiles. The wind often sang round the flagpole, and through the half-drawn curtains of the ground-floor window you could see faded maps on the wall and a stack of books on the windowsill. The house was uninhabited. Needless to say, I would have been the happiest of men had I been allowed to live in it.

I would have adorned it with new maps and books, and let it be aired through and through by the sea breeze and warmed by the sunshine, pink against the all-pervading blue.

The Austrian Beach

The Austrian beach was made for reading books that have to be read slowly, and set aside from time to time, while you dig about in the sand and by chance come across a fragment of rock crystal.

It was a wonderful place to doze. The wind from the sea tickled your eyelashes and the salt air stayed in your lungs and made you a little drunk.

Among the few people on the beach, I used to see Ilya Ilf (he was still known as Feinzilberg; the pen-name came later). I liked his quiet, sad face. He looked as though his head were full of half-dreams and half-stories and this was why he often fell asleep on the beach and had to be woken up at sunset.

Years later, I read some of the entries in his *Notebooks* and ever since I can't get rid of the idea that they all came to him just then, in 1921, on the Austrian beach. Here is one of them:

'I used to have soothing thoughts before I fell asleep. For instance, the English fleet sailing for Jutland: I looked long at the empty port and this lulled me to sleep. Tens of thousands of men were at sea. But the port was disquietingly calm and empty.'

'I looked long at the empty port.' There was no more usual and sad occupation in those days in Odessa, than looking at the empty port, and observing it in minute detail. The details were very attractive. The steady light, the heat of the noonday sun, and the taut waves playing nearby gave them all the vividness and beauty of the south.

I have been very active over the years. My activity often altered the course of my life and made me see it from new and unexpected angles.

But it never involved fuss, or useless chatter, or indiscriminate contacts with people.

On the contrary, it satisfied my thirst for observation – for examining life closely, as through a magnifying glass – and my desire to give it (in my imagination) much more poetry than it has in fact.

I could never help lending it extra colour and light, and the result pleased me, it increased its charm.

Even if I had very much wanted to, I could not have destroyed in myself this function which, as I understood later, is one of the essentials of the work of a writer. Perhaps because of this, my writing was to be more than an occupation or a job, it was to be my state of life, my interior state. I often caught myself out in living as though inside a novel or a story.

This need to look at life through a magnifying glass came upon me very strongly in Odessa and was no doubt connected with my wanderings about the port, and the peaceful hours I spent on the Austrian beach.

Time has worn away the biting sharpness of the sorrows and misfortunes of those days. Memory turns to them unwillingly. It prefers to see the brighter side and dwells on our rare joys. With the passing of the years they have grown in volume and significance. Neither typhus and famine, nor the cold in our little room and our complete uncertainty of tomorrow could destroy our faith in the happy destiny of the country.

Our youth was unconquerable. It would have turned Dante's Inferno into an exciting show. Our bodies swelling with hunger, we could still feel and rejoice in the scent of the first spring flower outside the window of our lodge.

Together with many of my contemporaries, I experienced and I remember those years as years of great and unshakable hope.

That hope was present to us always and in everything.

It reached us like a glimmer of sunshine through the heavy clouds of an Odessa winter day. All at once, a stalk of goosefoot in the yard, frozen and grey with rime, lit up with warm sunshine from no one knew where, and in this light we already felt the radiant approach of spring.

One day, Volodya and I were sitting on the Austrian beach when a short man with a lisp and languid eyes came up to us, a sailor's faded, shapeless cap in his hand.

The cap was full of apricots which he offered us.

After we had eaten them all up between us, he introduced himself as Evgeny Ivanov, a former correspondent of the *Russian Word*.

'You may have heard of me.' He smiled, showing small sharp teeth. 'I am known as an adventurer, but that's only one of those Odessa lies. I have a proposition to put to you, two propositions, in fact. Seriously, no joke.'

He put his cap on the back of his head and slapped me on the shoulder.

'Firstly – a paper called *The Seaman* is coming out in Odessa in a fortnight. You see before you its technical editor. I want you to work for me. I know you by hearsay. We'll have a paper to outshine the novels of Dumas *père*. Printed on special paper made of Saragossa seaweed. We'll hold all the seas in our fist just like that' – he clenched his little fist – 'and we'll squeeze stories out of them like orange juice, stories that will make collectors fifty years from now pay a hundred roubles for a back number of *The Seaman*.'

It was all lies of course. I looked at him. He was so carried away that he dribbled at the mouth like a baby.

'I'm not joking.' He laughed. 'I want you as assistant editor. Agreed?'

'Agreed,' I said without thinking.

Volodya refused a job on *The Seaman* on the grounds that he was section head at Oprodkomgub.

'Stick to your Oprodkomgub then,' Ivanov said haughtily, 'where you won't even get a tin of treacle so that you can give a ceremonial tea with maize rusks for the launching of our paper. You won't, you know. Well, my other proposition is simpler. Let's take our clothes off and go and gather shellfish on those rocks for supper. I've got the implement.'

He produced a jagged Austrian bayonet from inside his jacket.

Volodya didn't want to get his feet wet. He was an excellent swimmer but always bone lazy on the beach.

Ivanov and I undressed and waded out to the rocks.

'We can put the shellfish in my cap,' said Ivanov.

Gathering shellfish consisted in my lacerating my hands to prise them off the rocks with Ivanov's blunt bayonet while Ivanov collected them in his cap.

Our work was soon cut short. A woman's rough voice yelled from the beach:

'Zhenya! What d'you think you're doing? Come out at once!'

'Coming, Marina darling!' Ivanov called back ingratiatingly. 'I was only just . . . .'

'How long am I going to wait for you, you tramp?' came the voice, and at this point I saw her. 'Come out, I tell you. Do you want to catch pneumonia? If you don't care about yourself, you might at least think of the kids.'

'My wife,' Ivanov told me unnecessarily. 'Marina. She *would* turn up. A real bully. But she's a wonderful woman.'

Marina was huge, swarthy, ox-eyed and had a black moustache. Shaking hands with Volodya and me, she said:

'Come to supper this evening. I've got a piece of pork, we'll have it roast, with hominy. You don't know my Zhenya. Randy as a tom-cat, can't let him out of my sight. A real wolf. You wouldn't think it, a little chap like that, dainty as a ballerina. I will say, though, he's a wonderful journalist, for that he's really gifted. Only he will get himself mixed up in all sorts of stunts.'

'Shut up,' said Zhenya, hopping on one foot and pulling on his canvas trousers. 'Keep your nose out of my business. And my trouser belt is bust.'

'Has he asked you to join *The Seaman*?' Marina went on, paying no attention. 'You two will make a wonderful job of it. Only mind his tongue doesn't run away with him. He's got an impossible character.'

That was how I joined *The Seaman* on the Austrian beach, and I still think I was very lucky, as my subsequent story will show.

8
Glycerine Soap

Several things happened in the two weeks before I began to work for *The Seaman*. The saddest was the death of Torelli's sister, Rachel.

She caught spanish flu, then a new disease, had it very badly and developed complications.

Torelli stayed away from Oprodkomgub and looked after her like a nurse. Volodya and I often dropped in on her, although Torelli worried about our catching flu and kept trying to throw us out.

Volodya Golovchiner managed somehow to get hold of an old cake of glycerine soap and presented it to Rachel. Weak and feverish, she clasped her hands and blushed with pleasure so that her freckles stood out white.

We all examined the wonderful soap against the light. Golden and translucent, it still retained some of its subtle smell, though now rather stale.

One day Torelli had to go to town and needed someone to look after Rachel during his absence. He asked me to stay, but on condition I sat by the door.

By then I had left Oprodkomgub, so I was free.

Rachel lay with her eyes shut, smiling. She held the cake of soap in her hands, clutching it with her strong, violinist's fingers. She had studied under the famous Odessa violinist, Nahum Tokar.

Tokar was an excellent teacher, good at 'setting' his pupils' hands and 'giving them fingers', but a practical, down-to-earth man of no refinement.

'Is that the way to play this piece?' he would bellow at some wretched student. 'Where's the softness, the subtlety, the sweetness? Think of your mother, Rosalia Yosifovna, making her famous cherry jam. You're just going to eat it, and your mouth actually waters with anticipation. That's how you have to play it – with anticipation! Ant*i*cipate! Ant*i*cipate! Ant*i*cipate! Ant*i*cipate!' He beat time crossly with his foot.

Rachel seldom spoke of her music. Now she opened her eyes and said:

'Don't tell Abram, but I know I'm going to die soon. And he'll have me buried in that Jewish cemetery, next to Papa and Mama, and brother Arkasha. It's such a boring place! Now, for goodness sake don't start telling me I'm going to get well, and have cheeks like tomatoes, and perhaps marry a bonny lad in a cowboy shirt with a silver watch-chain. I've heard it all dozens of times from Abram. Better tell me where Majorca is.'

'Why do you want to know?'

'We had a lecture about Chopin, they said he lived there. I've never thought about it since, but today I've had a dream about it. There were hills, and very, very shallow streams running down into the valleys – the water was very clear and warm, and they were as wide as from here to the Quarantine Wharf. They flowed over green meadows, and there were all sorts of flowers growing in them, rising above the water and swaying with the current. I waded across the streams barefoot, and I liked feeling the soft grass under my feet.'

She turned her head and looked through the window. Small white clouds flew like canon-balls over the tops of the acacias, as though old bronze guns were firing them from invisible ships.

'There's a poet living here in Odessa,' I said, 'George Shengeli. I heard him read his poetry once, in Moscow, during the war. I remember only three lines: "There are islands distant as dreams – gentle as a quiet alto – Majorca, Minorca, Malta and Rhodes. . . ." I've forgotten the rest. Chopin did live in Majorca, with Georges

Glycerine Soap

Sand. In an abandoned monastery. He was very ill by then, dying, so the brilliant sunshine got on his nerves. . . .'

'Go on.'

But instead of waiting for me to continue, she said plaintively: 'Why did I have to be born into this family where everybody gets paralysed in the legs sooner or later? A legless, red-haired freak! That's not what I would have chosen! I'd like to sail in a rough sea, the wind grabbing at my knees! And to laugh, and sing! Does it disgust you when I talk like that? I'd sing you something now, only my chest feels so tight, as if it were strapped up.'

She broke off, and turned the glycerine soap over in her hands.

'Will you do me a favour?' she asked. 'Before Abram comes home. Pour some water into that saucer, and put the soap in it. And there's a dry bunch of flowers standing on top of that chest-of-drawers – get me a hollow stalk out of it, and bring it all here.'

I did as she asked. She split the tip of the stalk, dipped it in the soapy water, and slowly blew a large soap bubble.

It broke off, flew half way to the ceiling, and hung motionless in a dusty sunbeam, shining with pale, changing rainbow colours.

Rachel put her hand over her mouth, not to disturb the bubble with her breath. I, too, scarcely breathed.

'It's golden now,' said Rachel. 'A moment ago it was red like fire.'

She carefully blew another bubble, then a third, a fourth.

I picked a straw for myself, and also blew bubbles, so that soon the air was shimmering with their lights and colours.

A few landed on the floor and burst, but most of them kept afloat, playing in the sun, and sometimes joining into many-coloured constellations.

Downstairs, the front door clanged on its spring. The house shook. All the bubbles burst. Fine spray showered the floor.

'Hide it all away,' Rachel said quickly. 'I'm tired, I want to sleep. Now I'll never, never see it.'

'See what?'

'Majorca. Go now. Thank you. I don't feel very well.'

At the door, I bumped into Torelli. I told him his sister was asleep, and he turned back into the kitchen, to put the kettle on.

That evening he came to the lodge, sat down on the door-step, and burst into tears. Rachel had died, probably from heart failure.

Tears pouring down his face, he sat looking at us with round red-rimmed eyes and blowing his nose into a torn pillowcase.

I found an old bottle of valerian in Schwittau's book-case. Most of it had evaporated. I poured what was left into the tin I used as a glass, sat beside Torelli and gave it him.

He drank obediently, then let his head drop into his arms and shook with sobs. Gasping, pressing the pillowcase to his eyes, he kept apologising brokenly for giving me so much trouble, and for dripping tears on my torn and dusty brown velveteen trousers.

The doctor who signed the death certificate said that, were it not for the flu, Rachel could have lived a long time. Torelli told us how she had given a loud cry and suddenly stopped breathing.

The day of the funeral we all went to the house. In the room where Rachel's body lay, Gavarsaki stood in the corner, twisting his greasy cap in his hands. His eyes showed nothing except a pathetic effort to understand what was going on.

Prosvirnyak came in, looked disapprovingly at Rachel's feet in their wooden clogs and spoke in a low voice to the verger from the synagogue. The verger nodded obsequiously and shouted something to the old crones who were busy round the coffin. The shabby black coffin, 'hired' for the occasion, had obviously served a hundred times before to transport the dead from town to cemetery in the ramshackle hearse.

The crones fetched a torn brown shawl from somewhere, covered Rachel's feet, and the unfrocked priest went off with the air of having done his duty.

'Cheek!' Yasha muttered after him. 'Making himself at home, and giving orders.' But Prosvirnyak pretended not to hear.

I had never been to a Jewish funeral before. I was struck by the hurry of the proceedings. The hearse arrived, drawn by a scraggy horse in dusty funeral trappings. The garrulous old driver came into the room, rapped the lid of the coffin with his whip-handle and said:

Glycerine Soap

'Well, lads, who's the youngest? Grab it! Hoist it! All together! That's the way. Be careful at the bends. Whoever built that staircase, may he cough in hell, ought to be nailed up in that coffin instead of the young lady. Call it a staircase, it's a pain in the neck, so help me.'

Then we trudged along the cobbled streets, following the hearse. It jolted and swerved violently from side to side, as though trying to throw the coffin, like a restive horse its unwelcome rider.

The graveyard lay in the steppe, on the edge of the town. The steppe was burnt brown, although it was still early summer. Warm dust whirled in the wind against the high wall of the cemetery.

The wheel of the hearse caught on the gate-post. The driver had to back a little, but the horse refused to budge, so he beat it on the muzzle with his whip-handle.

Torelli shouted at him. The driver spat and said:

'Better cry over your sister instead of that skinny brute, if you are so soft-hearted.'

Torelli's eyes filled with tears. He stamped his little pointed shoes the colour of burnt orange peel, and screamed, all on one piercing note:

'Bastard! Swine! Moldavian thief!'

He was pitiful in his grief and anger.

The driver shrugged scornfully, lifted the back of the hearse, freed the wheel, then, without a backward glance, climbed into his seat, whipped up the horse and jogged away at a brisk trot, down the long graveyard avenue towards the grave. There was not a tree anywhere – all had been cut down for firewood – only the uniform yellow tombstones on either side of the unswept road.

The grave was a long way off. We ran after the hearse, together with a stumbling crowd of graveyard beggars.

The coffin was lowered into the ground. For some reason there was a lot of broken glass at the bottom of the pit.

Torelli gave alms to the beggars, a thousand roubles each (roubles had gone up in value). They accepted reluctantly, showing their dissatisfaction. One old woman with suppurating eyes flung the money into Rachel's grave and screamed:

Years of Hope

'What d'you expect me to buy with your money? The hole in the breadround? Buy it yourself, millionaire!'

We went away crushed. Torelli cried, off and on, all the way home. The verger hobbled beside him, saying:

'I don't know what the world is coming to, Monsieur Blumkis! I'd sooner lie in the grave myself than bury people like that, I swear by my mother's life.'

For several days after the funeral I went nowhere, only climbed through the window of the lodge into the garden every morning. Prosvirnyak kept the garden locked, so there was never anyone there. Only Prosvirnyak himself occasionally turned up, but went off as soon as he saw me, even his back looking indignant.

After Rachel's funeral, Volodya and I ceased to take any notice of him. No one else paid him any attention either, even as a landlord.

He resented this deeply and bitterly. It was about this time that he began to seethe with lust for vengeance, and his secret hope of an upheaval and the overthrow of the regime, turned into an obsession which unbalanced his mind. The less hope of change there was in fact, the more haggard he looked, wizened and wild-eyed.

He no longer said hullo to us when we met, but only muttered something about 'Jew-loving intellectuals' and 'retribution for the innocent blood of Christ'. He looked crazier and crazier. Even his cook, Neonilla, who never had a word to say for herself, refused to stay on alone with him and moved into our tiny box-room. She wept every day and told us how he had threatened to kill her for 'going over to the Jews and heretics'.

She also told us that Prosvirnyak, a widower, had become unfrocked after the February Revolution in order to marry a rich Greek (priests are not allowed to remarry). But on the eve of the wedding the bride lost her nerve, and took herself and her money off to Greece.

One night I was woken up by a faint scraping of metal on metal. It seemed to come from the kitchen, which opened into the box-room where the maid slept.

Glycerine Soap

I tiptoed to the glass door of the kitchen. In the garden, outside the box-room window, Prosvirnyak was squatting on his heels and working on the latch with a chisel.

He was too absorbed even to see me, his face wore a sly grin and he was muttering to himself.

Terrified, I cried out. He jumped up and fled, bounding across the garden into the yard and from there into the house, his old cassock flapping behind him like a pair of black wings.

I called Volodya. We went into the garden and looked at the window Prosvirnyak had been trying to open. Beneath it lay a five-pound weight and a German razor with a bone handle.

Volodya went for the police. Two hours later an ambulance arrived from the asylum. Two hefty male nurses tied Prosvirnyak's hands and took him away. He went quietly, moaning and whimpering to himself.

The maid left to stay with relations in Tiraspol. She was terrified of Prosvirnyak escaping and coming back to murder her.

Torelli moved soon afterwards. He was unhappy living in the flat where Rachel had died. A little later Gavarsaki was arrested for some unknown reason – probably the business with the ether. And one night the Professor of Ecclesiastical Law, a friend of Prosvirnyak's, who had occupied two of the flats, fled from Odessa together with his family.

By the end of summer, the building was empty. Boatswain Mironov moved in, a taciturn, red-haired native of Kherson, who was on *The Seaman*'s staff. For a bet, he could wrench the iron stakes out of the garden fence with one hand. After that everything was ship-shape in the house and garden.

I had only a few days left before I would start my job on *The Seaman*.

I read up all I could find in the Encyclopaedia about Majorca, Chopin, and Georges Sand, tried to recall everything I had ever read about them, and decided that nothing embellishes the events of our life like the passing of time.

Chopin and Georges Sand in Majorca lived a cheerless, difficult and unsettled life. Georges Sand had fallen out of love with the sick musician. Chopin was lonely, tormented by his cough, the pain in his side, and by the wind and rain at night. He knew he was dying, and would never compose the wonderful music of which his genius was capable.

His life was being cut short by his illness. Perhaps it need not have been. He searched his memory for the day of the irreparable mistake. If only it were given to man to know his mistakes in time, before they are past help! But this is given to no one. We all leave this life without achieving a tenth of what is in us to achieve.

In the ancient monastery, its walls green with damp, an iron crucifix in every cell, he murmured against God. Why did men implore Him to forgive their sins? How petty were their individual sins, compared with the great collective sin of bloodshed, lies and hatred He had permitted to be their lot!

Yet this was the God he praised in majestic music, in the pealing of the organ and the voices of the choir, sweet as heavenly strings.

The monastery corridors smelt of mould and decay. The forest moaned beyond the barred windows. And all at once the glamour of the romantic atmosphere he and Georges Sand had sought, paled before the image of the simplest, even the poorest – poor but warm – Lithuanian room with an unpretentious piano, plain but comfortable bed – and peace.

He was tired of being a genius. He had no more use for it. He bore the title, or the nickname, as a burden, pleasing only to his friends.

But as the time passed, it carefully dropped all that was petty and bitter from the life of Chopin and Georges Sand on the island, and turned that life into a poem of sacrificial love.

The poem touched many hearts, including the heart of a red-haired Jewess in Odessa, who had never in her life seen anything more beautiful than glycerine soap bubbles.

Wherever I went I took with me *The Romantics,* a novel I had started writing long ago, in Taganrog. I wrote at such long intervals that it was a wonder to me that I hadn't lost the manuscript.

Glycerine Soap

Now, in Odessa, I was working on the last chapters. As usual when I was busy writing, I became a savage. I avoided people, went off on my own, got up at two in the morning and worked by the light of the wick-lamp, afraid of Volodya waking up and asking me a lot of questions.

There was another odd thing I noticed about myself when I was working – if I was writing about something sad, I looked for sad situations and impressions, as though they could help me.

Early one morning I went to the Jewish cemetery, but soon came back, deafened by women's cries, hysterics, lamentations, frightened by the sight of sere old fingers clutching at coffins with such force that it took several men to pull them away, shaken by the silent weeping of widows, tearing their hair and trying to leap into their husbands' open graves. I came back troubled and confused by the sight of human grief naked and unadorned. .

One evening, just as I was finishing the last chapter, a thin, fidgety young man came to see me and said he was the future publisher of *The Seaman,* Isaac Livshitz.

'Not with an *f* but with a *v*,' he added. 'Livshitz, not to be confused with Yasha Lifshitz.'

'Don't you like him?'

'It's not that,' said Livshitz (I was never, from that evening, to call him anything but Izya, as did everyone else). 'But he won't last long in our time.'

'Why not?'

'He hasn't got much sense of humour.'

Izya gave me a note from Ivanov, asking me to come to *The Seaman*'s office next day – it was time to settle down to the job.

He had brought with him a tall, incredibly thin man who wore puttees, had the profile of a minstrel, and a lock of beautiful chestnut hair hanging over his brow. The man held out a large, warm, friendly hand, and clicked his heels. After that, he went to the book-case, took down the first volume of the Professor's Encyclopaedia, turned the pages and removed all the tissue paper which protected the coloured illustrations and maps.

'Eddie!' Izya said severely, but the man with the profile didn't

71

give him a glance. He took down the second volume and extracted the tissue paper from that. 'Now we'll smoke,' he said, pleased.

'Eddie! You mustn't! It isn't nice!'

The tall man silently tore a strip of tissue paper, pressed it with a kind of special skill between his fingers, put it to his mouth – and the lodge filled with the clear, high but ringing and undeniably touching sound of the song of some small bird.

'Is that nicer?' asked the man.

It was uncanny. I could hear the beads of sound forming in the warm throat of the bird.

'I'm so sorry,' Izya pulled himself together. 'I forgot to introduce you. Our Odessa poet and bird watcher, Edward Bagritsky.'[14]

'You got it wrong as usual,' Bagritsky said in a deliberately hoarse voice. 'You should have said, "Bagration-Bagritsky, last scion of the princely Caucasian-Polish family descended from the Jewish tribe of Dzuba." Let's go swimming at Langeron.'

9
Chopping Furniture

I would like to give the reader some idea of the remarkable man who was *The Seaman*'s editor, Ivanov, and of the atmosphere in his office.

Actually, the editor appointed by the Sailors' Union was Party-member Pokhodkin, former captain of an ocean-going liner. But Ivanov's drive, imagination and resourcefulness proved too much for him and the aged captain virtually gave up his job and retired to his villa in Arcadia.

Ivanov, who, as I have already said, went about in a squashed naval cap, patched cavalry greatcoat and clogs on his bare feet, looked like a tramp. But no one had greater charm than this innocent-eyed boy. He looked twenty although he was getting on for forty.

He was an excellent storyteller. His sense of humour never left him, however desperate the situation, and he was always courteous.

Even in those days he was not afraid to kiss a woman's hand. It was said that he had very nearly got himself shot for this in Ribnitza, a town famous for its pretty Moldavian girls.

He really had been a reporter on the *Russian Word*. This part of his complicated story was confirmed by the former manager of the paper, a God-fearing old man, named Blagov, who had fled from Moscow to Odessa. He also said that Ivanov had been the racing correspondent and had betted heavily on the tote.

Ivanov took on Blagov as senior proof-reader. Blagov turned out to be terribly fussy. The smallest misprint brought him down like a ton of bricks on whoever was responsible. Even Ivanov was afraid of him, not to speak of the compositors who trembled in his presence and looked like boys taking their school-leaving exam.

Ivanov was the kind of journalist who can find copy even in a ditch or a board meeting of the Society for the Insurance of Shorthorn Cattle.

Not only did he find 'copy' (the word at that time meant any interesting news) but he anticipated it. He knew where to look for it, he could tell from signs, known only to himself, what was going to happen and where.

In the same way he deduced from minute tokens, which no one else noticed, what people were likely to do. He knew what trifles can determine people's acts and motives. He was not afraid of rummaging among this litter and would often come up with 'a pearl, or a blood-stained dagger' or even 'an intrepid human heart', as our slicker Sukhodolsky put it.

An exuberant old man, Sukhodolsky would shout at us as he made up the paper:

'Do you know what our Zhenya could have been? A Balzac! A Balzac, I tell you. Or a Lombrozo!'

Ivanov had his own way of selecting his staff. He judged them by three qualities. They had either to be young and gifted (these had priority), or experienced and 'proven', or else barefaced liars and adventurers. Perhaps this was because he was himself a classical though harmless schemer, the very one who found the goose that laid the golden eggs.

He was always in the thick of new projects. Some he carried out in *The Seaman* – either successfully or landing himself in a major or minor row. But most of them had a life-span of a few hours. Ivanov gave them up with surprising lightness.

The first one he put through seemed to us interesting and in any case novel.

Above the heading, where every other paper carried the motto 'Workers of all lands, unite!', we were to print our own, a genuinely naval one – 'Workers of all seas, unite!'

A picture of the Vorontsov lighthouse duly appeared over the heading. It shed four beams, and the slogan was printed on them in four languages – English, Russian, French and German.

But the issue was the first and last of its kind. Ivanov was summoned by the Provincial Committee. He came back paler and more handsome than ever, and ordered the stereo to be destroyed at once and a new one made, still with the Vorontsov lighthouse and the four beams, but with the correct slogan.

When the blockade was lifted and foreign ships began to arrive, part of the edition was printed specially for foreign sailors in their own languages.

It was Ivanov who introduced this innovation which made *The Seaman* popular among foreign crews.

After that, we were besieged by translators. There was even an Abyssinian who turned up one day – brown, friendly and hungry. But as Abyssinia had no fleet, we had to decline his services.

He went away in tears. But Ivanov had a warm and generous heart. He brought him back, questioned him, and found out that Bartholomew (this was the Abyssinian's name) had been sent to Russia before the revolution to study at the university of Kazan and was now reduced to working as a barber. This gave Ivanov an idea: he appointed him official barber to *The Seaman*'s office which, literally, within a week of the first issue, had turned into a noisy club for writers and sailors. Plenty of people came in and out so the gentle Abyssinian was soon assured of a wide clientele.

The senior translator of *The Seaman* specialised in English and was a former shipping agent called Moser, fat, beaming, friendly and polite. He was a great expert on shipping, the intricacies of naval treaties and laws, and the cargo fleets and naval traditions of the world.

Wearing out the last of his English suits, he looked among us, skinny ragamuffins, like a veritable Lord of the Admiralty.

Our translator from the French was his wife. Tall and thin as an Englishwoman, a bit prim and very much the woman of the world, she struck us in those days as something of a museum piece.

She was an unusually conscientious translator. Every misprint made her ill, though in a lady-like manner. She lay moaning all day long on the dilapidated sofa in her room, sniffing the last remnant of her smelling salts and pressing to her temples a lace handkerchief moistened at the tap of the communal kitchen, where a certain 'Madame' Zofer held sway.

For hours on end, this imposing matron would shout her views in a deafening voice. Every sentence began with her favourite expression 'In days gone by. . . .'

'In days gone by I would not have dreamt of touching this hominy. I had the very best white bread every day. . . .'

A moment later her voice rang out again, but on a very different theme:

'In days gone by we gave birth to normal children, not like yours, my dear. God only knows what they are – kittens or something.'

At first Mrs Moser was embarrassed by Madame Zofer's loud and coarse pronouncements. But conventions are quickly shed, and very soon she was calmly telling me, as she sniffed her smelling salts, 'Wish she'd stop her barrel organ, that old tart!' and, by the end of a month on *The Seaman*, 'Madame' Moser was fluent in sailors' slang.

We printed anything in any way related to the sea and to sailing. After a while our hunt for suitable material became fiercely competitive.

At one time Mrs Moser looked like winning. She translated some marvellous poems by Tristan Corbière, a half-forgotten French sailor and poet. We printed a whole cycle with a biographical note by Jules Lafargue. It said that Corbière was a sailor from his boyhood up, always went about in clogs and a checked cloak, published his one book of poetry in Paris in 1873, and died soon afterwards while still a young man.

Lafargue wrote in his elegant French that Corbière's poetry was 'full of daring, strength, vivacity, tautness, and sad and stinging irony'.

But very soon boatswain Moronov, our Black Sea Street neighbour, snatched the laurels from Mrs Moser's feeble grasp. On an old English cargo boat, named with inexplicable tenderness, '*Heart of Ellen*' (it was a grimy steamer with patches of red lead on the sides and smelling of guano), he got hold of a manuscript called the *Sailor's Bible*.

It was written in Australian sailors' jargon and seemed to us a piece of folklore unique in the world.

Mironov had been lent several chapters. They had to be quickly copied out as the *Heart of Ellen* was leaving for Edinburgh in two days. (This was of course after the lifting of the blockade.) The whole office was kept busy copying under Mrs Moser's and Mironov's guidance.

The first chapter was on 'The Great Prayer'. This was the name given to the great slab of sandstone used for scouring the decks of sailing ships. There were other, smaller stones which were also named after various prayers – Pater Noster, Ave Maria, Mater Dolorosa and Miserere.

Scouring the deck with the Great Prayer was a form of punishment.

The *Sailor's Bible* described the hard lot of the sailors on the old sailing ships plying mainly between Europe and Australia around Cape Horn.

Whole sections were devoted to stale food, 'dog watches', illness, foul air in the hold, and the way to deal with these troubles in tropical waters.

A chapter on the 'Ocean's Cunning' covered every unpleasantness which a sailor could expect in the Atlantic and Pacific, especially in the 'roaring' forties. There was nothing vague about it; it described specific incidents remembered by generations of sailors: hurricanes, waterspouts, 'tsunams' (tidal waves caused by underwater earthquakes), storms and shipwrecks; and of course the omens feared on sailing ships (and other ships as well): St Elmo's fire at the top of the mast, blood-red rainbows, and the *Flying Dutchman*, its rigging hung with spiderwebs even in a storm.

There was also a 'Warning to Sailors' – the names of captains of whom sailors should beware (and a list of their crimes against their crews), a list of 'dirty dogs' – agents who 'shanghaied' men on board (mainly in the ports of Latin America and China); they made the men drunk and got them to sign unfair agreements. A list of dishonest tattooers; of bars in all the main ports, where sailors' possessions were taken as pledges; and of boarding houses where the lodgers were pursued by the Salvation Army.

The *Sailor's Bible* dispelled the more naive and romantic of our notions about the life of the toilers of the sea.

The facts themselves made you feel the anger built up over decades. The book was 'subversive', even though there was not a single slogan or appeal in it.

I am in a difficulty about Mironov. I should have liked to describe him here, but, having already published a story about him, I don't want to repeat myself.

I'll try to describe him as fully as I did in the story, but from another angle.

His most striking characteristics were his profound reticence, and his amused and friendly expression. This he reserved for those he considered to be 'real eccentrics'.

He had sailed from end to end of the Pacific Ocean. I doubt if even Stevenson could have done justice to his story, but in practice no writer would have attempted it because it was impossible to extract the facts from Mironov.

I managed to get only the main outline. Mironov was a revolutionary in the simplest sense of the word. To begin with, he was down on every dog of a captain and his underling, the mate. He believed in the mighty brotherhood of the workers, and that sailing was much the most suitable job for a revolutionary:

'Just look at the opportunities. You can spread the message all over the world, just like the wind spreading the smoke from the funnel. That's what you have to understand.'

It took me a good two months to establish, firstly, that Mironov had seen the first steamer 'made of glass', secondly, that he had spent two months in prison in New Orleans for having sided with the Negroes in a fight with the police ('We turned those policemen inside-out,' he modestly told me), and, thirdly, that he had been to

the Kergouelen Archipelago, known to sailors as the Island of
Despair.

There was nothing more I could get out of him, so I gave him up
as a bad job.

His recollections, if you could call them that, were mainly
climatic.

'Have you been to New Guinea?'

'Well, of course,' he replied dejectedly. 'Naturally. You can't
avoid it there' ('there' meant Melanesia). 'It's always sticking up
in your way.'

'What's it like?'

'What do you mean – like?'

'What sort of place is it?'

'Not bad,' Mironov replied doubtfully. 'Only it's as hot as a
steam bath. Wouldn't suit you at all.'

'Have you ever been to Peru?' I asked him another time.

'Yes, of course.'

'What's it like?'

'What do you mean – like?'

'What kind of a place is it?'

'A grave!' Mironov replied. 'Hot as a furnace and not a breath
of air. And the sea-water, incidentally, is like ice. You can't even
bathe.'

Mironov spent a long time in Odessa, waiting for a ship, so he
attached himself to *The Seaman* where he was used as a one-man
information service on anything to do with steamers and sailing
ships.

In these matters his knowledge was unequalled, even by Moser.
So Ivanov put him on the staff, but he couldn't think what to call
him, until at last Izya Livshitz suggested the grandiloquent title
'World Tonnage Consultant'.

The Consultant spent his evenings in Black Sea Street sitting on
a bench in the yard, smoking, gazing at the stars and softly singing
a Ukrainian song which had nothing to do with the sea:

> *Unharness the horses, lads,*
> *And lay you down to rest.*

He sang, smoked and enjoyed himself, never suspecting that his day of glory was at hand.

An enquiry came from Moscow, I think from the People's Commissariat of Foreign Affairs, about the cargo fleet which the Whites had taken away. It was easy enough to list the ships, but the Commissariat wanted to know what had happened to them: where they were and under what flag they were sailing now.

Moser threw up his hands. Who could possibly tell what had happened to all those ships! You might discover something from the foreign newspapers which occasionally turned up in Odessa, but only about two or three, if that.

He suggested calling in former shipping agents, captains of ships and experienced sailors generally, to see what we could get by cross-examining them.

The meeting was held. Cigarette smoke billowed out through the window like smoke from a ship's funnel. The experienced sailors sat in unbuttoned tunics and damp striped vests, they mopped their faces, their bald pates shone like beaten copper, they were hoarse and weary, but they knew the fate of only one steamer, and even that only approximately.

Meanwhile, Mironov had appeared in the office. Blushing crimson and catching at the chairs, he went up to Ivanov and said in a whisper that could be heard next door:

'Chuck it, Evgeny Nikolayevich! This won't get you anywhere. Get somebody to take it down and I'll tell you. You can check up later when you get the chance. I'll answer for any mistake with my life.'

The sailors looked at one another, grinned, moved up closer and waited.

Mironov took a chair at a distance from the desk, clutched his cap in both hands, fixed his eyes on the corner of the room lit by the sunset, where the delicate shadow of an acacia trembled on the wall, and began:

'Write down: Steamer *Grand Duke Alexis,* formerly owned by ROPIT, sold to Messageries Maritimes, re-named *Toulouse,* plies under French flag between Marseilles, Genoa and Corsica. The boilers have been cleaned but the French repair work is poor. The French crew are a poor lot but the first mate is still Grigory Pavlovich Mostovenko.'

The sailors stirred and sighed.

'Go on writing,' Mironov said, unruffled. 'Ocean going liner *Kostroma*. Belonged to the Volunteer Fleet, now sails under Italian flag from Brindisi to Massawa and Somali, calling at Alexandria. Painted white and re-named *Basilicata*. The boilers have not been cleaned, so her speed is very low. They keep her for non-urgent runs – in the back-yard as you might say. Crew – all black.'

By the time Mironov had gone through the list, a mother-of-pearl dawn was breaking over the sea, the first birds were twittering cautiously in the plane trees on the boulevard, and it smelt strongly of mattiola.

Nearly all the sailors were still there. They were pale with sleeplessness, and looked even paler in the chilly dawn pouring through the window.

Mironov's performance was amazing, inexplicable. He seemed to have the gift of total recall.

The sailors roused themselves, went up to him, firmly shook his hand and reluctantly went home; they wished they could go on talking about 'our sea and our ships', the ships they knew to the last sun-warmed rivet and scratch on the oak planks.

Mironov's fame spread across the Black Sea. It may well have reached Turkey and even Greece. Sailors have their own, rapid and mysterious postal service.

The Commissariat of Foreign Affairs sent Mironov a letter of thanks.

Embarrassed by his triumph, Mironov fled to his relations in Kherson, explaining, as he said goodbye to Volodya and me, that he didn't want 'this thing to go to his head'.

Before I finish with Ivanov, I ought to relate a number of incidents showing his intractable character. But for the time being one will do.

Most of the actions ascribed to his aggressiveness and wilfulness were due to his fanatical devotion to the paper. Nothing in the world mattered to him more than *The Seaman*.

His enthusiasm infected not only his colleagues but his wife Marina (she scolded him out of habit but no one took any notice), and his two little girls. There was no hardship he would have refused to bear, or his family to put up with uncomplainingly, for the sake of their beloved paper.

The winter of 1921 in Odessa was cold, windy and stormy. It seemed colder even than in Moscow because the porous stone of which the town was built let in the piercing damp of the seaside. Covered with a film of ice, houses and roads shone like enamel. The wind howled with misery in all the streets that ran from south to north; only in the narrow sidestreets did it lose a little of its strength so that you could recover your breath.

The joints of our fingers were again swollen and bleeding. The sea was frozen all the way to Great Fountain lighthouse. The Bulgarian steamer *Varna* lay caught in the ice-floes at the mouth of the harbour.

I found among the Professor's books an untouched calendar for the year 1916, and hung it on the wall, as some sort of reminder of the passing of time.

It seemed to pass more and more slowly, as though it were freezing up. Between the frost and the first warm days lay the thick wad of dusty, yellow calendar leaves.

The office was even colder than the lodge. It was housed in a large villa next to the Vorontsov Palace. The pale frescoes on the walls, and the stained-glass windows – especially the blue ones – chilled us to the bone.

We all huddled into one room, where there was an iron *bourzhouika* with a sooty pipe fitted to the window. Every now and then a smelly, oily liquid dripped from the pipe on to our heads and manuscripts.

Next to the *bourzhouika,* sat the typist Lucienna Hinson, a cheerful, noisy girl generally known as a 'Mediterranean beauty' and universally envied for her place in the room. But even Lucienna became soured.

Chopping Furniture

Kinti, the Rumanian manager who went about armour-plated in a thick black overcoat, had failed to produce so much as one armful of logs. He justified himself – unbuttoning his coat and beating the breast-pockets of his old field-jacket – by the fact that there was not a log to be found between Odessa and Vinnitsa, may he be hanged next to the Richelieu monument if there was.

'Stop beating the dust out of your jacket,' Lucienna snapped at him. 'And in general, do stop your "shmekeria".'

None of us knew what 'shmekeria' was, not even Lucienna, but it drove Kinti mad. He ran round in circles, grunting, wheezing, croaking, spitting, and seeming about to explode with a flash and a thunder clap – it was positively dangerous to be near him.

It took us several days to discover that the word was quite innocuous: all it meant was 'swindle'.

Finally, one day, life in the office came to a standstill. Our fingers could no longer hold our pens.

Then Ivanov ordered an oak sideboard as big as a Gothic church to be brought from the basement and broken up for firewood.

As I arrived at the office and was still in the icy entrance hall, I heard the cheerful sound of axe-blows and cracking timber, shouts, laughter and the fire roaring in our red-hot *bourzhouika*.

Inspired and pale with anger, Ivanov was directing operation break-up. He was furious with the owners of the paper, the Regional Water Transport Board, for not ensuring the supply of fuel to the office. Driven desperate, he had staked his all.

Just when the operation was in full swing, Kinti burst in, his hair standing on end, raised his arms to heaven and screamed that at this very moment a special, urgent, plenary, extraordinary session of the Water Transport Board was being held to discuss the lawless incident at *The Seaman*.

We merely chopped faster. The session took two hours and, by the time it was over, the sideboard and a china cupboard as well were in splinters. The wood lay stacked against the wall, and the *bourzhouika* roared like a squadron of planes.

Ivanov was severely reprimanded by the Board, and ordered to print the text of the reprimand in *The Seaman*.

One of our contributers was the satirist, poet and feature writer, Yadov, who wrote under the pseudonym of 'Boatswain Jacob'.

Ivanov commissioned him to write a poem on the chopping up of the furniture and published it in the next issue, with the text of the reprimand in small type underneath as an epigraph.

I remember only four lines of the poem:

> *The press is vital in our land.*
> *I'll guard it with my dying breath.*
> *My pen will never leave my hand,*
> *Nor shall my colleagues freeze to death.*

After the destruction of the furniture or, as they called it in Odessa, 'the chopping party', the Odessa naval authorities became more cautious in their dealings with Ivanov and hardly ever interfered with the running of the paper.

10

Linen Press-Cards

Before the revolution, *The Seaman* had been an obscure underground paper. Printed in Egypt, in Alexandria, it was taken to Russia by trusty people, usually stokers, who distributed it in various ports.

It came out at long and irregular intervals and looked more like a leaflet than a newspaper. One of its collaborators in those far-off days, an old member of the underground who had suffered some injury in the course of his work, had persuaded Ivanov to issue the permanent members of his staff with press-cards printed on fine linen, so that they could, if necessary, be sewn into the lining of a jacket or coat.

It seemed senseless to us. We knew that none of us would be sent on special assignments abroad, and refused to believe that we would ever have to go into hiding at home.

We chuckled over these extraordinary documents printed on long strips like tokens in a children's game and bearing a seal with two crossed naval anchors.

Difficult enough to unfold and decipher, the limp rags inspired nothing but distrust in all who saw them.

In the end, we put them away as souvenirs and, for practical purposes, were issued with ordinary press-cards typed by Lucienna.

The Seaman had other distinctive characteristics as well. It was not printed on ordinary paper but on the back of coloured stickers for packets of tea. No newsprint was available in Odessa. The stocks were only just sufficient for the main newspaper, *Odessa News*.

So, although the publication of *The Seaman* was authorised, we found that there was nothing to print it on. Luckily, Ivanov heard of a large stock of now unwanted Tsarist stickers lying in the customs shed.

Printed on thin, semi-transparent sheets, about the size of a double-spread, they were blank on one side and kept the printer's ink from seeping through the glossy papers.

The sheets came in various colours, depending on the brand of tea, but for some reason all pastel – mauve, cream, grey, pink, and so on.

Before the revolution the sheets had been cut into narrow strips and stuck round packets of tea. They showed the brand and the weight and were stamped with the Russian State emblem – a small two-headed eagle.

Because of the eagles, it took Ivanov a long time to get permission to use the stickers. He lost his voice arguing that printing the paper on them was in no sense monarchist propaganda.

We tried to keep to one colour for each day of the week – Tuesday was always mauve, for instance, and Wednesday pink – and usually succeeded in doing so.

Very exceptionally, for so-called holiday numbers, we were issued with white paper. But you could only call it white if you were looking at it in the dark. Grey, coarse and thick as wrapping paper, it was interlaid with large fine shavings of wood (you could even see the grain).

The ink would not take on the wood, so the holiday numbers looked striped and speckled. The letters were not printed but moulded by the type as in books for the blind.

But neither grey paper nor poor ink put us off. They made us even more devoted to *The Seaman* than if it had been slick and smart.

We put so much zest, effort and ingenuity into our work that the popularity of the paper was our best reward. The paper sold out in a flash. Copies were literally torn from our hands.

Linen Press-Cards

Apart from linen press-cards and sticker paper, *The Seaman* was distinguished by the number of devoted collaborators who were not paid a penny in cash. They were more than satisfied to work for a trifling fee in kind.

Whatever Kinti could get hold of was handed out: slabs of washing-blue as hard as cobbles, bent mother-of-pearl buttons, mouldy Cuban tobacco, rusty rock salt (it melted there and then, in the office, forming a corrosive red solution), and foot-rags of velveteen.

These good things were shared out between us by the irrepressible Lucienna. All she did, if anyone complained, was sing a comic song, imitating a cabaret singer and tapping the rousing beat with her clogs:

> *Endure a while,*
> *Hold on a while,*
> *The way is clear,*
> *The port is near!*

Everyone endured patiently, of course, and there were no complaints, not even from the recipient of the velveteen foot-rags.

Ivanov had issued sixty linen press-cards to permanent members of the staff.

But, besides its permanent staff, *The Seaman* had many worker correspondents and friends – people who nowadays would be called 'sympathisers'.

At first there were worker correspondents only in Odessa and the neighbouring ports – Ochakov, Nikolayev, Kherson, Ovidiopol, Zburyevka and Stanislavov. But the number grew as the Black Sea coast was liberated from the Whites. Soon they appeared in Rostov-on-Don, Taganrog, Mariupol, Berdyansk, then in Novorossisk and along the Caucasian coast and finally in the Crimea.

The Odessa worker-correspondents, from captains to stokers, used the editorial office as their club. All day long the kettle roared, Lucienna brewed carrot tea, and the rumble of voices, smokers' coughs and ringing laughter rolled over the waves of smoke-grey air.

As for the permanent staff, they were a mixed, noisy, ribald, picturesque community.

Occasionally the club was visited by 'old men' (by this we meant anyone over forty). There was the old bolshevik, Achkanov, a member of the underground in the days of the French occupation of Odessa, and a friend and exacting patron of *The Seaman*; there was the grey-haired and embarrassingly polite writer, Simon Yushkevich. But for the most part, the 'club' was composed of the fiery and impatient tribe of sailors and journalists.

'Learn to work and wait,' said Achkanov, as he listened to us. 'Socialism won't drop into your lap like dates from a palm-tree.'

We knew perfectly well that the revolutionary changes must take time, but we felt like skipping the hard, strenuous years and talking about the final outcome of the revolution – victory and happiness.

Sometimes we sat up at the club till dawn, and the golden light in the eastern sky seemed to us youngsters, in our lyrical mood, the glow of approaching happiness, a reflection of the golden age so near at hand.

The golden light in the sky merged with the golden glitter of the sea. Even the steppes of Dofinovka, on the far side of the bay, shone in the sun as though preparing to rejoice.

What didn't we talk about at the club! The mutiny on the *Potemkin,* the shooting up of the revolutionary cruiser *Ochakov* in Sebastopol, 'Execution Island' Berezan, the advantages of Kherson oak schooners, the qualities of Sanzheyka melons, the best way to clean the glass in a lighthouse lamp, the speed of red-mullet, the Greco-Turkish war, Barbusse's novel *Fire,* which had reached Odessa, how to repair a floating dock, make sheep's milk cheese, and shoot from captured Austrian Mannlicher rifles.

Listening to these conversations over carrot tea was rather like reading an encyclopaedia of revolutionary, literary, naval and current terms, only much better because what we heard was a living, vivid, racy, precise language, full of wonderful intonations.

It was a mine of linguistic ore, and probably that was why young

Linen Press-Cards

Odessa writers, who were later to become famous, spent their time at this revolutionary 'club'. A particularly frequent visitor was Edward Bagritsky.

As I can't describe all *The Seaman*'s contributors – although I wish I could – I will mention only a few, almost at random.

We had two feature writers – Yadov ('Boatswain Jacob') and the prose writer Vasily Reginin.

Yadov would perch on the edge of a chair and dash off his comic songs in a few minutes, without revising. By next day the songs were known to the whole of Odessa and a month or two later might well have reached Moscow.

Yadov was compliant and vulnerable. He would have had a hard life had it not been for the immense popularity of his songs with the workers and dockers of Odessa. This made him an asset to newspaper editors, cabaret managers and various music hall artists. He willingly wrote for them for next to nothing.

He looked very like a docker himself - bareheaded, in his faded blue smock, the pockets of his baggy trousers full of loose tobacco. Only his still face, gay and sad at the same time, made you think of an ageing comedian.

He was not the only one of his kind in Odessa. Miron Yampolski was a gifted poet and an expert on local folklore. His best-known song was 'Shneyerson's Wedding' ('It's terribly noisy in Shneyerson's house') which caught on all over the south. It contained some highly-coloured passages, such as the arrival at the wedding of the housing authorities to the strains of a swaggering march:

> *There comes the Chairman, milkman Abram,*
> *Complete with his suite like a Tsar. . . .*

The song and its sequel, 'Shneyerson's happiness was short-lived', could only have been written by a native Odessan who knew its suburban mythology inside out.

Nearly all the local songs were by nameless Odessan authors. Not even the city know-alls could remember who had written 'Hullo my Lyubka, hullo my love' – Georgie from Stevie's Street or Abram Knysh ('Do you mean to say you don't know him? –

That crook who got shot in the post-office hold-up in Tiraspol!')

The fashion in songs changed often. There was a new favourite at least once a year and sometimes once a month. The whole of Odessa sang them.

Anyone who knew them all could fairly accurately re-establish the chronology of the events in Odessa.

'Rostislav' for instance, and 'Diamonds' ('Our war-cry is "Serve the Republic, murder the public" ') were sung in 1918, while 'Denikin's unlucky, Budenny is winning, shall I go out and wave a red flag?' was sung in 1920 when Denikin's cause was lost.

I remember everybody singing 'Midshipman Johnson', then 'O these gloomy autumn days', 'Chicken', 'Two thieves broke jail in Odessa', 'My little daughter Bronya' and 'Manya comes into the Hall'.

After that came the more recent ones, such as the famous bandit song:

> *The C.I.D. is sending wires*
> *About the thieves in Kharkov town.*
> *They say the situation now requires*
> *Urgent action to put them down.*

This could be sung for ever, the name of the town varying at the performer's choice – Kiev, Yalta, Golta, Sochi or even far-away Vyatka.

Songs continued to pour from Odessa, but the stream was drying up; it ceased in 1941, on the eve of the war.

During the war the frivolous, garrulous Odessans, amateurs of comic songs and known as 'babbling brooks', fought with grim courage – though they still cracked Odessan jokes – and showed such daring and selflessness that even the enemy were astonished.

Old fishermen and sailors, for whom no room could be found on the ships, fought like the rest, desperately defending their Odessa, a town where work went with gaiety, as noisy and exuberant as the rolling waves of the Black Sea.

New songs came after the war, celebrating their feats and their unwavering love of their city.

Linen Press-Cards

In the spring of 1922, I left Odessa and spent several months in the Caucasus, in Batumi.

One day, I came across Yadov sitting alone, hunched up, on the Promenade. An old straw hat pulled down over his eyes, he was drawing with his stick on the sand.

I went up to him. We were both delighted to meet again and went off together to eat at the Miramar.

The restaurant was crowded and smelt of shashlik and purple Isabella wine. There was a string orchestra (this was before the days of Jazz and few people had even heard of saxophones). It played a pot pourri from various operettas, then struck up Yadov's famous song 'Bubliki'.

Yadov grinned, examining the wine-stained tablecloth. I went up to the leader of the orchestra and told him that the author of the song, Yadov from Odessa, was there.

All the musicians came over and stood round our table. The conductor raised his hand and the rollicking tune thundered out under the smoke-blackened vaults.

Yadov stood up. Everybody else got up too and clapped. He offered the musicians wine and they toasted him with flowery speeches.

Yadov was moved, he thanked everyone, but whispered to me that he would like to leave at once.

Outside, he took my arm and we went towards the sea-front. Yadov leaned heavily on my arm, limping a little. The sun had almost set. Far away, a violet mist hung over the Anatolian coast and above it a fiery band of smouldering clouds. The streets smelt festively of mimosa.

Pointing with his stick at the clouds, Yadov said suddenly:

> *'And like sleeping nature's dreams*
> *Billowing clouds drift by. . . .'*

I glanced at him in amazement. He chuckled.

'That was Fet,' he said. 'He's like the rabbi in Brodsky's synagogue.[15] But seriously, you know, I was never meant to be a clown, especially in verse. I was meant to be a lyrical poet. But there, I never made it. No one ever told me that, in all circumstances of life, you must fight like a savage. On the contrary, they taught me, from my childhood up, to bow and scrape. And now it's too late. Now poetry flows past me like a river in spate, and I stand on the bank, and look and love and envy. But I can't write anything real. There are too many silly tunes playing in my head like on a xylophone.'

'But don't you write lyrical poetry for yourself?'

'Certainly not! I still have enough intelligence and taste left, thank goodness, to know that that's all finished for me. There are people who are conscious of their gifts, of their genius. Well, I'm conscious of my impotence. That's tougher. Can you remember who was that quite outstanding German poet who suddenly one day sat down and wrote doggerel? All his talent had evaporated. Apparently, he had treated it with a carelessness amounting to criminal negligence. After that he never wrote anything worth while again. It wasn't even fit for the gutter press. So he changed his profession and took to concocting poison out of bedbugs. Even that was more useful. To humanity.'

'It's a sin to talk like that, Jacob Semyonovich,' I said, genuinely horrified.

'My dear chap, I've thought it all out long ago. I'm not in despair. I know I frittered away my talent on a lot of greedy, cheeky, commercial entrepreneurs. But if I hadn't, and were still alive today, I might have written a second Marseillaise. Anyway, thank you for your kind words.'

We said goodbye. The first raindrops fell from the dark sky. I walked home quickly, listening to the steady noise of the rain approaching from the sea.

I never met Yadov again but I remember his sad clown's face with the deep creases round the mouth and the tragic eyes.

Every writer and journalist in Russia knew Vasily Reginin ('Vasya' as he was called by everyone all his life).

I met him through *The Seaman* in Odessa, but had already heard about him from Yasha Lifshitz, Blagov, Ivanov and the other older journalists.

Linen Press-Cards

The most improbable tales were told about him, they sounded more like anecdotes. He seemed to have the kind of daring rarely shown by Russian journalists – rather like Stanley who pursued Livingstone to darkest Africa out of sheer sporting instinct. In Russia there was scarcely another journalist of Reginin's sort. Yet in everyday life he seemed a reasonable, even a cautious man.

He had lived in Petersburg before the revolution and edited several cheap and reckless 'yellow' periodicals such as the *Blue Journal* and the mass-consumption *Argos* and *I Know All*. He did it with imagination and go, and had his own circle of readers.

Serious people were used to the dull but high-minded *Russia's Wealth,* the staid *European Herald,* to *Niva* with its magnificent supplements, to the *Journal for All* and the progressive *Chronicle*. The omnivorousness of Reginin's magazines, well-illustrated but merely entertaining, put them off.

But the yellow journals multiplied. Inevitably they began to compete. Chasing after subscribers, they resorted to low stunts such as the *Blue Journal* competition for the best grimace. A valuable prize was offered.

There were many competitors, and photographs of people pulling faces appeared in issue after issue.

The circulation went up, but the competition could not go on for ever. It was time to think of something new and equally striking.

An announcement appeared in the Petersburg press: on such-and-such a date, at the Cinezelli Circus, Vasily Reginin, editor of the *Blue Journal,* would go into the tigers' cage, alone and unarmed, sit at a table where he would be served coffee and cakes and, after a leisurely meal, walk out unscathed.

Photographs and a full report, including Reginin's first-hand impressions, would appear in the *Blue Journal* which reserved all rights.

The day of Reginin's rendez-vous with the tigers, the circus was packed to the roof. Mounted police cordoned off the building.

Reginin, his face thickly powdered and a chrysanthemum in the buttonhole of his frock coat, calmly walked into the tigers' cage, sat down, and had coffee.

The tigers were stunned by the impudence. Huddled in a corner of the cage, they gazed at him in fear, growling softly.

No one breathed. Attendants with fire hoses stood close to the bars.

Reginin finished his coffee and, still facing the tigers, backed to the door and swiftly stepped out.

At that moment the tigers, realising they had missed their prey, leapt after him with a terrible roar and, clawing at the bars, tried to tear them down.

Women fainted. The public howled with delight. Children cried. The attendants soused the tigers with cold water from their hoses. Outside, the mounted police held back the seething crowds from the doors of the building.

Reginin threw his fur-lined coat over his shoulders and strolled out casually, twirling his cane.

I only half-believed this story until Reginin showed me the photos of himself and the tigers. 'I was just a kid then,' he said, making a face. 'I was showing off. Still, it certainly bumped up the circulation.'

I knew Reginin in middle age and as an old man, and I noticed that he kept a touch of the buffoon to the end of his days. It showed in his jokes and in his taste for the unusual, the flashy, the garish.

When he left Odessa, he went to Moscow and edited one of our most interesting periodicals, *Thirty Days*.

All his experience as a journalist went into it and it was a brilliant job.

Thirty Days serialised Ilf and Petrov's *Twelve Chairs* at a time when all other periodicals and publishers preferred to keep away from this amazing but frightening story.

Reginin collected the best writers and poets, and all the promising youngsters (who have since become established authors and even 'classics'), and made them work for *Thirty Days*.

He told me with offhand pride that all the writers and poets of the thirties, without exception, had contributed to his magazine. As all paths lead to Rome, so these writers, particularly the beginners, were led to *Thirty Days*. No wonder there is still a saying among them:

'Old Reginin picked us out
And blessed us with his dying breath.'

His whole way of working (his 'style' as they say now) was alive and quick, and free from red tape.

He would take a manuscript, look it over quickly, say with a casual, almost bored expression, 'Right, make out a receipt for three hundred roubles', pull out the drawer of his desk and count the roubles out. Then he would sigh, as after a hard job well done, and begin one of the conversations for which he was famous – news, anecdotes, recollections, literary sketches, jokes and epigrams.

He had had a long and interesting life, and his memory was sharp as a razor. He told endless stories but hardly ever wrote anything down, which is a great pity. His Memoirs would have been fascinating.

He died a few years ago, painfully but bravely. His courageous last days on earth were the epitome of his life, a restless, seething life devoted to journalism and to art, the life of a man who loved nothing in the world better than sensations, books, the theatre, the circus, and the friendship of gifted men.

That was how I remember him in Odessa, and I found him unchanged in Moscow, after many years of work on *The Seaman*: lean, elegant, with the face of Adolphe Menjou, quick movements, a quick patter, and sharp yet weary eyes.

II

The Stolen Speech

One evening in mid-April, when the sky beyond the office window was turning green and the Vorontsov lighthouse blinking red, Izya came quietly into my room. He softly shut the heavy door (carved with bunches of grapes and garlands of roses), tiptoed to the desk, and pressed his finger to his lips.

He was panting with excitement.

As the office was empty – everyone had gone home except Bartholomew the Abyssinian – I thought Izya's antics unnecessary.

'All right. What is it?' I asked in a loud voice.

He rolled his eyes, squeezed my shoulder and whispered under his breath:

'Quiet: listen.'

He told me – drawing back to look at me triumphantly and searchingly – that he had just been to the Provincial Committee's press and there he had seen. . . .

He choked, broke off, clumsily rolled a cigarette, lit it, took a deep pull and told me what he had seen.

He had seen the text of Lenin's speech on the New Economic Policy.[16] Lenin had recently made it in Moscow. It had been set up as a pamphlet but not yet printed. The text was preceded by a note on the front page to the effect that this was a confidential document with a restricted circulation – i.e. for initiates only.

There had been vague rumours about the speech for the past three days, but no hard news. All we had heard at the office was that a speech had been made and, of course, published throughout the Russian Federation. But in Odessa, for some reason, it was being kept from the public.

We were sure that this was a decision of the Provincial Committee. Evidently they disagreed with Lenin's basic propositions. We heard later that we had been right.

On the other hand, it was difficult in those days for people like Ivanov, Izya and myself, who were not in the party, to have a clear view of what was happening. We knew nothing for certain. We were only angry that Lenin's words were being kept from the people. We thought it a crime. We simply had to get hold of that text and publish it, whatever the cost.

We had tried but failed. At the Provincial Committee, we were told with a grin that it was none of our business and we shouldn't be too nosey. But now Izya had caught sight of the speech by accident. The forme was in the glassed-off office of the manager of the press, and the manager had gone out for a minute. Izya had not been able to read the whole text; there were no pulls lying about, and he couldn't very well hang around indefinitely. He had only dropped in to see the manager about a stereo for the *The Seaman*. Naturally, he showed no sign of having seen the forme, and went away at once.

'We must either publish that speech,' said Izya, 'or admit that we are cowards and nitwits. I don't want to be either a coward or a nitwit. Nor do you. So listen to my brilliant plan. Sukhodolsky works three days for us, and three days for the Provincial Committee. We must get him to hand over the forme to us for two or three hours at night. That will give us time to take it to our press, print the speech as a supplement to *The Seaman,* wash the ink off and bring it back. Let's go and see Ivanov. He's the only one who can persuade Sukhodolsky.'

We went at once. Ivanov lived a long way off, near French Boulevard. Hearing about the speech he turned white and began to stammer. This was always a sign that he was terribly excited.

We went with him to the old sandstone house where Sukhodolsky lived. Izya and I waited at the gate. The hands of my watch seemed to have been smeared with glue. The seconds hardly moved.

Years of Hope

Time dragged and our cause seemed lost. Sukhodolsky would never take the risk. Izya kicked the wall hard in frustration.

At last Ivanov came out with Sukhodolsky. Sukhodolsky was beaming. 'Clever lads!' he whispered mysteriously. This was his highest expression of delight.

It turned out that Sukhodolsky's father-in-law was night watchman at the Provincial Committee's press – 'a pearl of a man!' Sukhodolsky said.

Sukhodolsky willingly took charge of the operation. Everything went swiftly and silently. With Sukhodolsky's and the watchman's help, we brought out the heavy lead forme, put it in a cab and drove to our own press. There, Ivanov had everything ready – paper from the store and trusty compositors he had asked to stay behind. (The current issue of *The Seaman* was nearly printed, so they would normally have gone home.)

We held a council and decided to print the speech as a special supplement. The pages of the pamphlet were wider than our columns; only four would fit into our page instead of six, leaving a wide blank at the side. But there was no time to fuss. The forme was placed in the machine. Sukhodolsky made up the headings. The tea-wrappers rustled and the machine hummed, printing the historic speech.

We read it avidly by the light of a kitchen oil-lamp. History was being made here beside us, in the dim press room, and we had our small part in making it.

The supplement printed, we carefully washed off the ink, carried the forme to the cab, and Izya and I took it back to the Provincial Committee press and put it back exactly where we had found it.

No one saw us except the silent watchman. We left no trace.

We were too excited to go home – it would be light in an hour anyway – so we went to the office.

Bartholomew opened the door, welcomed us and put on the kettle.

We sat on stacks of wrappers and drank tea. Aurora showed up in her dusty pink cloak.

We were all proud that in the morning Lenin's speech would be known to the whole of Odessa. We were not worrying about the consequences of our daring, though we knew they could be serious. Only Sukhodolsky shook his head and said it might be a good thing to disappear from Odessa for a while.

And that morning, the 16th of April 1921, the news-vendors of Odessa, soured, sceptical, sclerotic old men, shuffled off in their wooden clogs, shouting hoarsely:

'*Seaman*! Comrade Lenin's speech! Exclusive. You won't get it anywhere else. *Seaman*!'

The Seaman sold out within minutes.

Odessa hummed like a hornets' nest.

We expected trouble and were prepared for it. But none ensued unless you count my meeting with the Provincial Committee Secretary in Greek Street.

Purple in the face, he was rushing headlong, brandishing a copy of *The Seaman*. He pulled up short in front of me and shouted:

'Thieves! Our forme! . . . Gutter press tactics! . . . You'll answer for it. You've gone too far!'

'Not at all,' I said innocently. We hadn't stolen anything. Where was the proof?

He choked. 'You want proof, do you!' He pulled out the supplement. 'There you are. Every misprint is ours. And the wide column – that's ours too. There's your proof!'

He stuffed the paper into his briefcase and vanished amidst the dying acacia blossom.

Whether we had learned to be ready for the unexpected or were young enough to have kept a remnant of childish exuberance, we felt nothing but pride in our exploit.

It raised us in our own eyes, though we didn't talk about it.

We were no longer just reporters. The sense of being citizens, of taking part in the life of the country, filled us with joy.

12

The Alleged Death of the Artist Kostandi

Chekhov was terrified of Odessa reporters. He hated talking about his unfinished work anyway, and always added:

'For God's sake don't tell an Odessa reporter.'

Some of those who had so frightened him were still among us. They were the last surviving 'kings of scoops'. The *Odessa Post* was their home, and its editor, Finkel, their patron.

The paper carried almost nothing but detailed reports of thefts, robberies, confidence tricks, bandit raids and murders.

The style of the articles was incredible. I remember a leader on some trifling decision of the Town Council, in which Finkel wrote: 'For joy at this decision, we should paint our Odessa sky pink and applaud the Town Council from the roof-tops.'

The older journalists told us youngsters that Finkel's name was indeed a legend but only because of his abysmal ignorance.

Only one of the reporters who had terrified Chekhov had attached himself to *The Seaman*. Lyova Krupnik was a man of deceptive appearance. A mild looking old gentleman with a honeyed voice and gold pince-nez, he went about in a patched tussore jacket, exhaling an Ancien Régime aroma of triple eau-de-cologne.

But, in spite of this innocent air, Lyova was as dangerous as a bomb primed with mustard gas. Ivanov had warned me, but I disbelieved him until an unusual incident took place.

The Alleged Death of the Artist Kostandi

In summer, I used to go to the office very early. I liked walking slowly from my Black Sea Street, choosing any one of the four possible ways. They all led to the Boulevard and the Vorontsov Palace.

There, the nasturtium blazed like fire, clinging to old pillars, and the wind from the port breathed – breathed, not blew – fresh, salty, and filling the street with a smell of newly-scrubbed decks.

I sat down on the low wall overlooking the harbour, and closed my eyes the better to feel the breath of the wind on my face. Apart from decks, it smelt of acacias, dry seaweed, the camomile in the cracks of the sea wall, and of tar and rust. Occasionally, all these smells were washed away by a special after-storm smell from the open sea. It was quite unlike, and could not be mistaken for anything else. It was as though a girl's arm, cool from bathing, were brushing my cheek.

I sat on the wall, losing count of time, inwardly absorbed in the contemplation of the shimmering horizon of Golconda. I wanted to believe – and I believed – that this flowering land existed somewhere on earth. At times, it seemed to be sailing towards me, ever nearer and more luminous, driving before it the waves of wind, the currents of soft air.

After dozing for a little on my bench, I went on to the office. Bartholomew, our Abyssinian barber, opened the door.

He slept in the once luxurious drawing-room with its flaking frescoes on the walls. They showed the Goddess Aurora, in her transparent pink cloak, flying amidst beige clouds and strewing the earth with crimson flowers and acanthus leaves from a horn of plenty.

It always touched me that the simple artist had painted as a background the Odessa watersteps and monument to Richelieu, enveloped in a blue mist from the sea.

My room was still fresh from the night air. I sat down at my desk and managed to get through some writing 'for myself' before Lucienna turned up (she always came in later than I did). I was thankful for these quiet hours in the empty office.

Then the contributors arrived and piled my desk high with long strips of paper covered with writing. All day long I corrected articles, despatches and news-items. I worked until I was ready to drop and my arm was stiff and aching. I had to rewrite about half the news-items, to rid them of their irrepressible Moldavian-Odessa style.

In the end I came to enjoy sub-editing and correcting. It helped me with the revision of my own work.

I was assistant editor and therefore general dog's body. I did everything from editing to allocating the reporters' jobs, and from interviewing authors to settling the blazing rows between old and young reporters.

After all that, Izya and I spent the evening making-up the next day's issue.

One morning I arrived very early and found Lyova Krupnik in my office. He sat on the windowsill, crying and wiping his eyes on a spotted handkerchief. His pince-nez swung at the end of its black cord in time to his sobs.

I asked what was wrong. He waved me away as though my question had been out of place and indiscreet. Apparently his sorrow was so great that he was beyond answering questions.

I offered him a glass of water. He drank it with his tears and said brokenly:

'Lying on a table.... Covered with a sheet.... And we were at school together. . . . We shared a desk for eight years. . . . We were penniless together in Arnautov Street, and now. . . .'

He gave another sob, blew his nose and looked up with swollen, red-rimmed eyes, asking for sympathy.

'Have you lost a relative?' I asked diffidently.

'Oh no. I've got none, thank goodness.'

'Who then?'

'Kostandi, the artist,' he cried in a tone implying I was an idiot to ask. 'The leader of the South-Russian school,' he said more quietly. 'A master! Brilliant! And a heart of gold. The kindest man in the world.'

He was so miserable that I began to feel genuinely sorry for him. I couldn't think of what to do to comfort him. At last I had an inspiration and said:

'Pull yourself together now, and sit down and write an obituary. For tomorrow's paper.'

Lyova caught his pince-nez, put it on crooked, got off the windowsill, dusted his trousers and said querulously:

'You might at least give me some paper. What am I to write on? There's never a quarter of a sheet for a cigarette in this office.'

I gave him some old galleys but he sniffed and said they might be all right for the sort of news and articles we published but not for a great artist's obituary. It was positively indecent and insulting to his memory.

He was being difficult, but I thought he was upset and gave him a few sheets of good paper – it was worth its weight in gold in our office.

He went off to the next room, and spent a long time blowing his nose, sighing and scratching with his pen.

Lucienna came in, heard that Kostandi had died and said:

'That dear old man! Why does it always have to be people like him, and not bastards like Kinti and all the other twerps who only know how to swindle people!'

'Oh, dear!' said Lyova. 'I wish you wouldn't use such coarse language, Lucienna Kazimirovna. It breaks my heart to hear you.'

'Fancy that, you poor shrinking violet,' Lucienna replied. 'Don't you pretend you're so cut up, I won't believe you.'

Lyova dictated the obituary, and he and Lucienna quarrelled because he insisted on two carbon copies and Lucienna swore she had only one decent carbon left. In the end, he got his way and left, apparently taking his carbon copy as a souvenir.

I read the obituary, corrected it (where Lyova said Kostandi was as great as Raphael) and sent it to the printer.

Thinking of Lyova going home so wretched, I said to Lucienna:

'You really shouldn't persecute that poor defenceless old man.'

'Who's wretched and defenceless? Krupnik? You wait, one of these days he'll play you such a dirty trick, you'll curse the day you were born. All you Moscovites are the same, you're too sentimental.'

Just then our proof reader came in, Kolya Hadzhayev, a young student from Novorossisk University, and a great connoisseur of art and poetry.

His judgments were brief, harsh and without appeal. No one dared argue with him because none of us had his erudition.

He despised all who differed from him, regarded them as 'trashy little people', rather like a species of cockroach, and never spoke of them without making a face as though he were going to be sick.

Of all Odessa poets, he tolerated only Bagritsky; he spoke condescendingly of Narbut, and considered George Shengeli decadent as a poet and because he went about in a topee.

'Have you heard?' Lucienna asked him. 'Kostandi, the artist, has died.'

'He's no artist, he's a pig-breeder, your Kostandi,' Kolya, black with anger, shouted unexpectedly in reply. 'How can you so belittle the word "artist"! All his life he held on to the apron-strings of the Itinerants.[17] Don't talk to me about him!'

The reporters were beginning to arrive. Arenberg, thick-set and with a cheerful face, came in. Every piece of news, from the arrival of the Norwegian steamer, *Camilla Gilbert*, to an earthquake in Arabia, filled him with uproarious joy. It was the course of life itself that delighted him, its gossip, the details of its movement, all its changes – whether the result was good or bad was also important but of secondary interest.

Hearing of Kostandi's death, Arenberg commented that of course Kostandi was no Repin.[18] This produced another outburst from Kolya, not against Kostandi, but this time against Repin.

'That old crank who stuffed himself with hay!' he said, and went off without a glance at anyone, despising us all.

Repin had had certain mild eccentricities, among them his belief in the medicinal properties of soup made from fresh hay. This angered Kolya more than anything else.

Then Ivanov came in with Lowengard, a tall, grey-haired reporter with a Don Quixote beard and a cane like a short lance.

The Alleged Death of the Artist Kostandi

Having spent his life covering the Odessa port, which he knew like the back of his hand, he said he could not express an opinion about Kostandi, the artist, as he had never heard of him, but of course he had known Kostandi, the captain of the steamer *Toiler of the Sea*. . . .

He was interrupted and went to sit in a corner, immersed in his thoughts, eyes closed and hands crossed on his stick. That was how he usually sat.

Even when I was not on duty, I often went to the press in the evening to check the make-up of the paper, have a chat with Izya or Sukhodolsky and, in general, for a breath of the press-room air.

Working at *The Seaman*, I became addicted to typography. Even the smells of printer's ink and lead were 'sweet and pleasant' to me. I came to like the compositors, their jokes, their background of wide though random knowledge, their ruthless judgments, and even the way they swayed back and forth in front of the type-case, like Moslems at their prayers or reading the Koran.

The dark, dusty, low-ceilinged room, the damp galleys, humming machines, stacks of coloured tea-wrappers and rolls of paper, the traditional savage fights with the proof readers, the tea cooling on the windowsill, the geranium in the window, the smell of its rough leaves – everything had a romantic glamour for me, I suppose because it was here that papers, books, maps, posters, calendars and shipping schedules started their life.

I don't think I'll ever forget the rough deal table, sticky and black with ink, under the open window. Beyond it and the rusty grating, the leaves of the chestnuts drooped in the heat. I remember the purple sheen of the asphalt outside, and the damp proof of a poem by some unknown poet:

> *August sunset. A taut breeze*
> *And the breath of distant fields.*
> *And snow-white clouds rising,*
> *Almost blue, over the sea.*

The galley had 'grief' instead of 'sea' (*'gorye'* for *'morye'*), and the proof reader had made a note in thick blue pencil in the margin. It occurred to me that the compositor hadn't done so badly. Why shouldn't clouds rise over human grief, as emblems of halcyon beauty to distract and heal the heart?

But that night the press-room was in an uproar. Even from the street I could hear Izya's indignant voice and the guffaws of the printers.

The moment I came in, Izya rushed at me, waving the proofs of Kostandi's obituary, still damp from the press.

'Who produced this horrible thing?' he yelled, white as a sheet with rage.

'Krupnik.'

'I knew it, the bastard!'

'Why? What's the matter?'

'Oh, nothing much.' He grinned ferociously. 'Just a fascinating little incident. May a windlass knock his brains out, that King of Reporters. Only that I was coming here to make up the paper and, two doors away, whom did I see but Kostandi risen from the dead! I even walked with him as far as Catherine Street, and he told me about his picture exhibition next month! And he took my hand in his manly grip, and I actually noticed a smear of blue oil paint on his tussore jacket. And he didn't look like a corpse, let me tell you.'

'But what does it all mean?'

'It means that all Krupnik told you was a pack of lies. He wanted five thousand roubles, so he sold you a pup. You'll say it's crazy, *The Seaman* can sack him. So it can, but Finkel never sacked anybody in his life, so he thinks he can get away with anything here as well. He's a born liar and nothing will change him as long as he lives. It's the only thing he'll never let you down on.'

'I'd like to squash him flat, that louse,' said Sukhodolsky. 'I can't bear to look at him. I break out in a sweat whenever I do. It's that lying voice that turns me up.'

We cut out the obituary. Next morning, it was not in *The Seaman* but the identical text, down to the last comma, appeared in the *Odessa News*.

Arenberg rushed in, beaming with the sensation in journalistic circles, and told us that Krupnik had gone straight from *The*

The Alleged Death of the Artist Kostandi

Seaman to the *News*, and palmed off the obituary with the same crocodile tears as he had shed in our office.

The *News* offered its deepest apologies to Kostandi, and *The Seaman* printed a poem by Yadov:

> *If in your paper you have read*
> *That you are dead, you must be brave.*
> *If that is what the press has said*
> *Be quick and nip into your grave.*

Krupnik vanished. Ivanov, furious, ordered him to be brought in, dead or alive. But he was nowhere to be found. He had not spent the night at home.

A fortnight went by. One day, I arrived at the office very early as usual, walked into my room and stopped dead. There, on the dirty windowsill sat Lyova Krupnik, crying his eyes out. His pince-nez dangled on its black cord and swung to his shuddering gasps.

'I'm so sorry,' he said brokenly. 'There was a slight mistake.'

'A mistake?' I asked, my hands growing cold.

'Yes,' he nodded meekly. 'A mistake made in good faith. It appears that the man who died wasn't the artist Kostandi, but Kostandi the shoe-black. It was the same surname and the same address; the shoe-black lived in the basement. You can see how the confusion arose.'

'Just a minute.' I pulled myself together. 'Didn't you see him with your own eyes, lying on a table under a sheet?'

'That's just the point.' Lyova blew his nose. 'It was in the basement, it was dark, and there was the sheet as well. Incidentally, I'll be doing a piece for you on Kostandi's exhibition. It's coming soon.'

'Posthumously, I suppose.'

'That's a nasty crack,' Lyova said reproachfully. 'In fact it's in very poor taste.'

'Look here,' I said. 'Go away will you? You've got nothing more to do with this paper!'

'Fancy that!' he replied cantankerously and got up. 'Call it a paper! A cheap rag! I was the Odessa correspondent of the *Figaro,* so you needn't throw your fish-wrapper in my face.'

I had no time to answer. The door flew open. On the threshold stood Ivanov, livid with rage.

'Out!' he shouted in a clear, metallic voice. 'Get out at once!'

Lyova Krupnik jumped and trotted to the door, clutching his pince-nez.

We heard him spit angrily on the floor of Aurora's drawing-room, and his clogs drum on the pavement as he left *The Seaman* for ever.

The last of the reporters whom Chekhov had rightly dreaded had gone from our lives.

13
What do you want, Young Man?

The heroic style is well nigh forgotten: modern life demands simple expression.

Yet how describe the indescribable – the Odessa market known in the twenties as the New Bazaar?

How make it come to life for readers unused to rhetoric? How depict yesterday's typhus patients milling round red-hot frying pans of garlic and sliced Ukrainian home-made sausage – the first offering of the NEP[19] – writhing and crackling in its own fat?

How convey the noise of swearing, howling, whining, shouting, curses and hysterics, all merging into one continuous roar and suddenly cut off by the piercing sound of a policeman's whistle? Or the stampede of the black marketeers, festooned with their belongings, over the wooden pavements shaking to their tread? Or the trail of yellowing bust-bodices, soldiers' cotton underpants, and cracked, liver-coloured, rubber hot water bottles left in their wake?

Since rhetoric is out, I will have to do with every-day words.

There were certain unwritten rules you had to know before it was any use your going to the market.

The first was never to show interest in any of the goods, and preferably to look bored as you elbowed your way through the crowd. Because at the smallest sign of your looking for something to buy, dozens of people would clutch your arm, your shirt, or even your coat belt from behind, and shout with desperate voices and tragic eyes:

'What do you want to buy, young man?'

No one asked you what you wished to sell, because the answer was obvious: what a man wanted to sell, he carried on his arm or round his neck. If he had nothing on display but his eyes darted in search of a customer, all the regulars knew at once that he was selling fake jewellery and called after him:

'What crown jewels have you pinched today?'

Only very exceptionally was it impossible to tell at a glance what a man was dealing in.

This was the case of the French sailor, nicknamed Lyova. He had jumped his ship and stayed on in Odessa, convinced that, in those fabulous days of civil war and the collapse of international order, no one would report him as a deserter to the French government.

Short, unshaven, sullen, with a hooked nose and fierce, scornful eyes, a beret with a red pom-pon on his head and a torn purple muffler round his neck, he would race silently along Deribasov Street, his hands thrust deep into the pockets of his dirty blue greatcoat, and suddenly shout in a piercing falsetto which could be heard streets away:

'The best! The strongest! The most lasting!'

He never said what he had to sell. His flight was like a whirlwind. The crowd weaved round him and pressed back against the walls. Some out-of-town visitor would ask: 'What's he selling?' But the Odessans only grinned and shrugged. Small boys hooted after him. A policeman came hurrying from the nearest post, whistle in hand.

Only when he saw the policeman, would the sailor cry his wares:

'Very best flints! For lighters! The longest! For lighters!'

With this triumphant cry, he vanished into the far end of Sadovaya where the New Bazaar smouldered in the fumes of vegetable oil – a refuge for speculators, pick-pockets, and once-rich old ladies.

He was a very statuesque figure, that sailor, modelled in terra cotta and painted in bright colours.

Another rule was always to accept the first price you were bid.

What do you want, Young Man?

Neglect of this unwritten law could end in disaster, as happened to me.

Vasya Reginin's wife, a graceful, fragile and unpractical young woman, fell sick.

In addition to a wife, Vasya had a little girl of six, named Kira.

Sick with worry himself, he dashed about the town, trying to get hold of a little money, and some remedy unattainable at that time (mustard plaster, I think). He begged me with tears in his eyes to flog the expensive wadded interlining of his coat in the market.

The wadding was thick, and light as down. I thought it must be worth a fortune.

Why he picked on me, I don't know. He said I was clever at knowing my way about, and he was useless at this sort of thing. I fell for his flattery, collected the wadding from his flat, rolled it up and went to the Bazaar. It was foolish, but I had no idea of where I was going – I strolled along Sadovaya, not suspecting that it was the road leading straight to hell.

At first, no one would even look at the wadding. They behaved as though they had never heard of such a thing. 'What's that?' they asked. 'Stuffing for a divan? Or a shawl for a premature baby?'

I was annoyed, but kept my temper, even when cheeky women pulled out tufts, divided them into strands and, for some reason, smelled them.

At last, a kind old man with an inch-tape round his neck (presumably a tailor) offered me a hundred thousand. But I had made up my mind to sell for no less than two and get Reginin out of all his troubles.

'Are you crazy?' said the tailor. 'Take it and don't play Baron Nobel. You're lucky to have come to an honest man.'

I refused. He shuffled about, then spat and went off, crying:

'Breeches! Made while the customer waits, from his own material, in two hours! Fit like gloves! We give them away! Three thousand roubles without the trimming!'

The next offer came from a tipsy Greek and was for seventy thousand. Then a whining woman offered me fifty.

It was nearly four o'clock and the market was beginning to empty. The Greek reappeared with an offer of thirty-five thousand.

I told him to go to hell. Then a young man, barefoot and in an old Cossack cap, pushed a ten thousand note into my hand and tried to jerk the roll from under my arm, saying:

'Go on, take it and get back to your girl friend.'

I snatched the wadding back and threw the money at him.

'Oh, like that, is it, you bastard?' said the young man, reaching into his shirt-front.

At that moment, a woman in a hat with velvet pansies screamed. She was selling off the last of her potato pies, shrivelled and dry as string. In answer to her shout, a policeman blew his whistle. The young man strolled away with an independant air, the shoulder muscles rolling under his thin shirt.

'Go away quickly,' the woman said to me. 'He's got a knife under his shirt. I can't stand always seeing bloodshed in the Bazaar, and having to give evidence.'

It was getting dark. My day at the market had come to an inglorious end – or so, in my abysmal ignorance, I believed.

I left the Bazaar. As I was walking away, I suddenly remembered having seen the tipsy Greek, the whining woman, and the boy in the Cossack cap, all three together behind a stall, at the beginning of the market-day. Only then did it dawn on me that the same gang of 'Mavericks' had been working on me all day. 'Mavericks' were thieves who operated a ring in the market, and pilfered and robbed when they got a chance.

At the market gate I saw the Greek again. He was smoking a crumpled cigarette, and ignored me.

I walked on, and became aware of a disgusting, pungent smell following me. At the corner, a woman who was selling sunflower seeds called out:

'You're on fire, young man! You're smoking like a chimney!'

I looked round. Thick, white smoke poured from the wadding.

I unrolled it: a glowing, smouldering pattern was spreading over it.

I tried to stamp it out, but it wriggled like dozens of little fiery snakes, and only spread further. The only thing left was to kick the burning, smoking mess off the pavement.

'You must have got into bad trouble with the mavericks,' said the woman. 'So they set fire to your wadding out of spite. Must have lit it from behind, with a cigarette.'

I thought of the tipsy Greek at the gate. This was clearly his work.

A crowd had gathered round the smouldering heap. The woman told them my sad tale, indignantly shouting and gesticulating.

I went straight home. I was choking with disgust, anger and shame. I cursed those who thought there was any glamour about thieves and robbers. What rubbish! What a tale for trusting fools!

I swore a solemn oath never again to go to the Bazaar.

Next day, I had somehow to get hold of two hundred thousand roubles – the amount I had promised Reginin for his wadding. After racking my brains for a long time, I decided to go to Moser. He was reputed among us to be a man of substance.

The Mosers were full of sympathy and indignation; they gave me tea and two large sheets of money (a hundred thousand roubles each). I rolled them up and went to Reginin's. Never in my life before had I felt so cheerful as I did that morning.

The third rule of the Bazaar (as illustrated by this incident) was never to carry anything on your back – for the obvious reason that it could be slashed with a razor or set on fire and, later, bought for nothing as damaged goods.

In spite of my oath, I could not keep away from the market for ever. Almost the only goods in the State shops were calico, some wadded jackets, and hats with ear-flaps.

The hats, made of artificial fur, were for some reason delivered pressed into huge bales. No one unpacked the bales, and they lay about in the shops, smelling of decay.

I was always having to go to the market, if only for my fishing rods and hooks.

Every time, I came away crushed and humiliated by the sight of shameless greed, helpless poverty, trampled human dignity, bestial coarseness, and trickery and deceit.

The swindlers were legion – petty, shifty-eyed and impudent.

Gamblers played, cheated and fought, hiding behind the stalls. Caught in the act, cardsharpers howled, smeared blood over their faces and swore such refinements of vengeance that your blood ran cold.

Newspapers were tied to the rags of wandering madmen and set on fire.

A dense crowd would collect in some secluded corner of the market. Eyes glittering with curiosity, passers-by would join, and push silently forward, closer to the centre, where you could hear the sound of dull blows and muffled groans. A thief was being savagely beaten, or a woman, suspected of pilfering, searched and stripped naked to the delighted guffaws of dishevelled market women from out of town.

Occasionally, the thief tore himself free and, grimacing, battered and bruised black and blue all over, broke into the parady of some obscene dance; or the naked woman and the one she had robbed clutched each other's hair and, together, rolled over and over in the dust.

Never before had I seen such a concentration of malice and depravity in any one place. It was all the more astonishing and sad, because the warm, sparkling sea, the humming city, the blossoming acacias, the walls touched with gold by the sun, were so very near. Despite the famine, there were many laughing people in the streets, the air smelt of flowers and, low over the sea, the stars twinkled like light-buoys.

Still, there were some good people even in the Bazaar. They were all cranks, people with broken, empty lives, but here their goodness shone like a beacon.

I remember an old man, half blind, who sold photos for stereoscopic viewers. He was always surrounded by children. All day, he would show them views of Paris and Rome, Moscow and the Island of Madeira for nothing. It was hard to see how he made his living, for in those days, no one except Izya Livshitz went in for stereoscopic photographs, and even Izya bought them only out of pity.

The old man kept a dusty globe with faded colours standing on the pavement beside him. For fifty roubles you could spin it and look at fascinating places like Easter Island, or the Zambesi River, or the city of Caracas.

A little further on there was a graphologist-fortune-teller. He told fortunes from hand-writing. All day long he sat on a bench and examined envelopes and letters through a huge magnifying glass.

He was always scolding his clients, and even shouting at them. But they were devoted to him all the same, especially the women.

'Haven't I told you three times running, citizeness – you must leave that man you're living with, or you'll land in jail with him.'

'I suppose I ought to, really,' the woman agreed vaguely.

'Do leave him, Vera,' her friends urged her. 'You can see this man is saying it for your good.'

'Am I a social parasite or some such scum,' the fortune-teller grumbled, 'to extort money from you at the rate of three hundred roubles a time, all because of your havering. If you don't want to do as I tell you, don't come to me. I'm not going to tell your fortune again, I've had enough.'

Another time, I heard him shouting:

'From the way you form your letters, you must think a lot of yourself, young man. You swagger about like some sort of a von Baron or von Dingdong. But a right attitude to life can be achieved only through study and patience, not through insolence and yapping. I've been watching you a long time – always about with that Vitka Ten-of-Spades, instead of doing an honest job and making your old parents happy.'

But the most endearing of all was old Zusman who sold caps in a little back-yard shop with a signboard. 'Warsaw Caps'.

He sat in his shop with his assistant, a dismal, sickly boy called

Milya. The boy slept and snored, while Zusman, his spectacles perched on the end of his nose, slowly read the newspaper, and sighed, glancing disapprovingly at his rare customers.

One day, I went to the shop with Yasha Lifshitz.

'What d'you want a new cap for?' Zusman asked Yasha crossly. 'The one you've got on is all right.'

'That's my own business,' Yasha replied, equally crossly.

'Oh, well, if you enjoy chucking your money away on caps! Milya, show the comrade a cap. I've got to see a neighbour.'

With that, he went off. Snorting with annoyance, Yasha tried on several caps. Milya held the mirror for him, and nearly went to sleep and dropped it.

Yasha could not make up his mind. He put on a brown cap, and asked me if it suited him.

Before I could answer, Zusman returned, glanced at him, and asked Milya:

'Where's that customer who dropped in just now?'

'That's him,' said Milya wearily, pointing at Yasha.

'It can't be!' Zusman drew back, clasped his hands, and broke into a happy smile. 'I don't believe it! You're making it up. The one I see is a real lord in a Scottish cap. A proper Lord Chamberlain – and that one was very shabby, more like a tramp, if you'll forgive my saying so.'

'It's him all right,' Milya insisted glumly. 'He's just got a different cap on.'

'Ai-ai-ai!' cried Zusman. 'See how a cheap, hundred-rouble cap can change a man! If it's made by a proper craftsman, of course. It's miraculous, what it can do!'

Yasha couldn't help laughing, and Zusman, delighted with his trick, laughed until he cried and gave him a friendy slap on the shoulder.

'We have to be artists in our trade,' he said, still laughing. 'Honestly, I'd have made a good comedian! Come and have a chat one day. I could die of boredom in this empty shop. I'll make you such a cap for the summer as even Lloyd George never had in his life, nor ever will. The only snag is getting hold of the material.'

What do you want, Young Man?

Everyone was happy, and Milya back on his stool behind the counter, nodding and snorting.

'How would you like to have that to talk to all day?' Zusman sighed. 'Honestly, it's enough to drive you mad and send you to your grave.'

'What do you want, young man?' I was asked at the Bazaar. All I really wanted was to see this heap of misery and filth burnt and scattered to the winds. And so it was in the end.

Reginin, incidentally, never doubted that I had sold his wadding for two hundred thousand roubles. Only twenty years later did the truth come out in Moscow, and Reginin, shaking with his usual silent laughter, gave me the two hundred thousand back, in the form of two ten-rouble notes of the 1939 issue.

14
I Promise you Maupassant

The Seaman printed a short story called 'The King'. It was signed I. Babel.[20]

It was the story of an Odessa bandit chief, Benzion ('Benny') the Scream, who married off his ageing sister Dvoira to an ailing, whining thief. The thief married her out of terror of Benny.

This was one of the first of Babel's 'Moldavanka' stories.

Moldavanka was a district near the goods station, with a population of two thousand bandits and thieves.

He had moved into the district to study its ways. He stayed with an old Jew, Tsires, who was being scolded into his grave by his shrewish wife, 'Aunt Khava'.

Soon after renting a room from this meek old man, who looked like a Liliputian, events were to develop at breakneck speed and Babel had to flee for his life from the flat with its overpowering smell of fried onions and moth-balls.

But more of this later.

'The King' was written in a precise, terse language. Its freshness hit you in the face like a splash from a syphon.

Ever since my schooldays the work of certain writers had seemed to me a form of magic. When I read 'The King' I realised that a new magician had joined their ranks, and that nothing he wrote could ever be limp or colourless.

'The King' dealt with a world completely outside our experience. The characters, their motives, their circumstances and their vivid, forceful talk – all were strange to us. The story had the vitality of a grotesque. The smallest detail showed the sharpness of the author's vision. And suddenly, like a burst of sunshine through the window, you came upon some exquisite fragment, or the unexpected rhythm of a sentence balanced like a translation from the French, measured and rich.

This was new, exciting prose. It had the tone of voice of a man still covered with the dust of the Cavalry Corps campaigns,[21] but who could draw on all the riches of the culture of the past – from Bocaccio to Leconte de Lisle and from Vermeer of Delft to Alexander Blok.

Izya Livshitz brought Babel to *The Seaman*'s office. Never had I seen anyone look less like an author. Stooping, almost neckless because of his hereditary asthma, with a duck's bill of a nose, a creased forehead and an oily glint in his little eyes, he was anything but fascinating. At first sight you would have taken him for a commercial traveller or a stockbroker. But this, of course, was only until he opened his mouth.

At his very first words everything changed. His voice had an undertone of insistent irony.

Many people couldn't bear to meet his eyes; they drilled through you. Babel was a born unveiler of truth. He enjoyed cornering people, and was known in Odessa as an awkward, dangerous man.

He arrived at the office with a book of Kipling stories under his arm.

Talking to the editor, Ivanov, he put it down on the desk but kept looking at it with greedy impatience. He fidgeted in his chair, got up and sat down, obviously on edge. He wanted to read, not to make polite conversation.

He soon changed the subject to Kipling, saying that everyone ought to write his kind of steely prose, and to visualise in the clearest detail what he was about to write. A story should be as accurate as a military report or a bank cheque. Even the handwriting should be firm and clear, as on a cheque or an army order – which Kipling's, incidentally, was.

He finished on an unexpected note. He took off his spectacles, and this at once gave him a benign and helpless air.

'We Odessans,' he said with a hint of mockery, 'will never have our Kipling. We are peaceful hedonists. But we will certainly have our Maupassants – because we have plenty of sea and sun, and pretty women, and plenty to think about. That much I can promise you.'

He went on to tell us of his visit to Maupassant's last flat in Paris – the sun-warmed frilly pink lampshades, like the under-clothes of expensive courtesans, the smell of brilliantine and coffee, and the vast rooms which frightened the sick author, who for years had schooled himself in the tight framework of his plots and the shortest way of telling a story.

Babel recalled with delight the Paris he had known. He had an excellent French accent.

From some of his comments and questions, I realised that Babel was a man of incredible persistence, tenacious as a leech, wanting to know everything and never squeamish about the truth, a man outwardly sceptical to the point of cynicism but who, in fact, believed in the simple goodness of the human soul. He was fond of quoting the Bible: 'Strength makes thirsty; sorrow slakes the heart.'

I watched him from my window as he walked away along the shady side of Marine Boulevard. He walked slowly, for no sooner had he left the building than he opened his book and began to read. At times, he stopped to let someone pass, but not once did he look up.

People went by and glanced back puzzled, but no one spoke to him.

Soon he disappeared in the shadow of the plane trees, their velvet leaves fluttering in the stream of Black Sea air.

After that, I often met Babel in town. He was never alone. Swarming round him like midges were the 'Odessa literary boys'. They caught his jokes in mid-air, flew round the town with them, and ran his countless errands without complaining.

He told them off for carelessness, and drove them away ruth-lessly when he had had enough of them. But the rougher he treated them, the better they seemed to like it.

I promise you Maupassant

Nor were they alone in their hero-worship of Babel. Old, established authors (there were several in Odessa at that time) treated him with as much respect as did the young local writers and poets.

The reason was not only that he had exceptional gifts – it was also that Gorky liked and appreciated him as a writer, that he was just back from Budenny's campaigns and shared in their legend, and above all, that he was our first authentic Soviet writer.

It has to be remembered that Soviet literature at the time was scarcely born, and that not a single new book had reached us in Odessa except Blok's *The Twelve*[22] and a Russian translation of Barbusse's *The Fire*.

They produced a shattering impression on us – they already flashed with the distant lightning of new poetry and prose, and we learned Blok's poems and the austere prose of Barbusse by heart.

It was not till late summer 1921 that I got to know Babel really well. He was living at Ninth Station in Fountain. I was on holiday, and Izya and I rented a dilapidated villa not far from his.

One of our walls overhung a sheer cliff. Chunks of bright pink plaster often broke away and went skipping gaily down to the sea. So it was safer to sleep on the verandah facing the steppe.

Our garden stood waist high in grey weeds. Tiny poppies, the size of finger nails, struggled through them and looked like drops of fresh red paint.

We saw Babel often. Sometimes we spent nearly all day on the beach, fishing for bullheads and listening to Babel's leisurely stories.

He was a wonderful storyteller. Those he told were even more powerful and accomplished than those he wrote.

How can I describe that gay yet sad summer we spent at Fountain in 1921? It was made gay by our youth but sad by the vague anxiety continually in our hearts. And also, perhaps, because of the pitch-black southern nights. They dropped their curtain right in front of us, on the top step of the stone verandah.

You could stand on the verandah and stretch your hand into

the night and snatch it back, having felt the chill of cosmic space at your fingertips.

The gaiety was in the bright patchwork of our conversations, jokes and hoaxes (the Odessa word for them, 'roulette', soon spread to the rest of the country).

The sadness was unaccountably embodied for me in a clear light which shone on the horizon every night.

It was a star low over the sea. It watched us with friendly insistence night after night, yet none of us knew its name.

The sadness was also, for some reason, in the smell of the stone highway as it cooled in the evening, and in the light centres of the wild verbena growing outside our door, and in our strong sense of the quick passing of time.

The world was still beset by troubles. But for us youngsters they were already next-door to happiness, because the times were full of hope of a rational outcome, of an end to persistent misfortune, of the flowering bound to follow the seemingly endless winter.

That summer, I think I understood for the first time what is meant by the 'power of genius'.

Everything was made absorbingly interesting for us by Babel's presence. We lived in his reflected light.

The people I had met until then had rarely made a lasting impression on me. I forgot their faces, voices, their words, their way of walking. But now they etched themselves on my memory.

Babel often returned from Odessa by the evening horse-tram (it had replaced the electric tram, now forgotten). The tram went no further than Eighth Station, and you could hear it from a long way off, clanking all its loose bolts.

From there, Babel walked, and arrived dusty, tired, but pleased.

'You should have heard two old women talking in the tram! About eggs! Let me tell you. You'll laugh till you cry.'

He described the conversation, and we not only laughed until we sobbed, we rolled on the floor, helpless.

Then Babel would pull us each by the sleeve and ask in the querulous voice of the market woman we knew at Tenth Station:

I promise you Maupassant

'Have you gone completely barmy, young fellow? Or what?'

You had only to close your eyes when you listened to him, and there you were, sitting in the Odessa tram, looking at the passengers with as much insight as if you had been their bosom friend all your life. Perhaps they didn't really exist and Babel had made them up from scratch. But what did we care so long as we could see them in front of us, complete, living, earthy, grunting, coughing, winking at each other and nodding at Babel, who already was said in Odessa to be as clever as Gorky.

Long before the stories were published, Babel told us about old Guedalla who dreamed of an 'International of men of good will', and the incident with the salt at Fastov Station, and the furious cavalry charges, and Budenny's dazzling smile, and we heard from him some wonderful Cossack songs. There was one he liked particularly; we often sang it afterwards in Odessa and its poetry never ceased to astonish us. By now I have forgotten all but a couple of lines:

The star of the fields above my father's house,
And my mother's grieving hands . . .

It was that 'star of the fields' that got me every time. I even dreamed of it at night, a quiet, solitary star high up above the dark, familiar, barren fields.

Babel was a ready talker, and told us much about Gorky and the revolution, and how he, Babel, once took up unofficial residence in the Anichkov Palace in Petersburg, and slept on the divan in Alexander the Third's study, and took a peep in the desk, and found a box of cigarettes presented by the Sultan of Turkey, Abdul Hamid. They were fat, pink cigarettes with an Arabic inscription in gold. With an air of great mystery, Babel handed us one each, and we smoked them that evening on our verandah. A delicate aroma drifted over Ninth Station, but we both got splitting headaches and, for a good hour, reeled like drunkards, clutching at the walls.

It was then I also heard from Babel the strange story of Tsires.

Babel stayed with Tsires and his sluggish, morose wife, Aunt

Khava, at the very centre of Moldavanka. He had decided to write several stories about this suburb of Odessa and its turbulent way of life. He felt drawn by the strangeness and originality of such undoubtedly gifted natures as the already legendary bandit Mike the Jap (Benny the Scream). He wanted to study them closer, and Tsires's dingy flat was the obvious look-out post.

It stood firm as a rock amidst the rampaging violence of the thieves' dens and the deceptive respectability of quiet homes, with crochet mats and silver candlesticks on the sideboard, where bandits sheltered under their parents' roof.

Surrounded by daring and well-armed young men, the flat was as safe as a fortress with an armed guard.

When Babel confided the purpose of his research work to Tsires, the old man was anything but pleased. In fact he was frankly worried.

'Oi, Monsieur Babel!' he said, shaking his head. 'And you, the son of such a well-known papa! And your mother a famous beauty in her time! Courted by Brodsky's own nephew, they say. Take my word for it, Moldavanka is no place for you, writer or no writer. Forget it. I'm telling you here and now, you won't have a pennyworth of success here, and you might collect a pocketful of trouble.'

'What kind of trouble?' Babel asked.

'Do I know?' Tsires replied evasively. 'How can I tell what crazy notion even a peaceful man like Five Roubles might get into his head – not to speak of Lyuska Chicken and the rest. Better not risk it, Monsieur Babel. Go home quietly to Catherine Street, to your papa. I tell you honestly, I'm sorry I ever let you that room. But how could I refuse such a pleasant spoken young man!'

Sometimes Babel spent the night in his room at Tsires's and heard Aunt Khava scolding the old man in whispers for letting a stranger into the house.

'What will you get out of it, you old miser? A wretched hundred thousand a month! And for that you'll lose your best clients! Lazar Broide will have a good laugh on you. They'll all go over to him, I swear by our late Idochka.'

I promise you Maupassant

'The cops are only waiting to jump on your Broide,' Tsires said uncertainly.

'Mind they don't jump on you first. He'll ruin you, that lodger. Nobody will give you one per cent. What will become of us in our old age?'

Tsires worried, tossing and turning in his bed.

So did Babel, trying to guess what Aunt Khava meant. He didn't like these mysterious conversations at night. He felt they hinted at some dangerous secret.

The nights were long in Moldavanka. A bleary light from a distant street-lamp fell on the peeling wallpaper. The walls smelt of acetic acid. At rare intervals the sound of brisk, businesslike footsteps came from the street, or a high-pitched whistle, or even a shot close-by, and a woman's hysterical laugh. It came from behind brick walls. The sobbing laughter seemed to be immured in them.

Rainy nights were particularly bad. Water tinkled in the drain-pipe. The bed creaked at the slightest movement, and all night long something nibbled at the rotting timbers behind the wall-paper.

Babel felt like going home to Catherine Street. There, behind thick walls, his room was peaceful, dark, safe, and the manuscript of his latest story, revised and re-written a dozen times, lay on the desk.

Babel would go up to it and stroke it gingerly like a half-tamed beast. He often got up at night and re-read three or four pages by the light of a wick-lamp, hemmed in by thick dictionaries standing on their side. Every time he found a few more unnecessary words and triumphantly crossed them out. 'Language is clear and power-ful,' he used to say, 'not when there is nothing more to add to a sentence, but when there is nothing more you can cut out.'

All who saw Babel at work, especially at night (though few ever did, as he went into hiding when he wrote) were struck by the sadness of his face and its unusual expression of kindness and distress.

During those barren Moldavanka nights he would have given

much to go back to his manuscript. But, as a writer, he felt he was a soldier on reconnaissance, who must put up with any hardship in the way of duty: the loneliness, the stench of the extinguished oil-lamp which brought on his attacks of asthma, and the screams of tormented women from behind the walls of the houses.

One such night it suddenly dawned on him: obviously Tsires was a common 'crib-spotter', a scout for thieves, who tipped them off about the places they should raid. He got his 'cut' – his percentage of the proceeds. That was how he made his living. Babel was indeed an inconvenient lodger!

He could frighten away Tsires's reckless yet cautious clients. Who would want to take an extra risk because stingy old Tsires, tempted by an extra hundred thousand, had let a stranger into Moldavanka's very heart?

And the stranger had turned out to be a writer and therefore twice as dangerous as any ordinary card-sharper or pimp!

At last Babel understood Tsires's hints about 'a pocketful of trouble' and decided to move out in a few days. He needed these few more days to get Tsires to tell him all the interesting things he knew. For Babel was conscious of his powerful gift for squeezing people dry, gutting them with ruthless persistence or, as they said in Odessa, 'drawing their very souls out of them.'

But this time he failed. A bandit, Simon Lop-Ear, beat him to it, and there was nothing metaphorical about the way he parted Tsires from his soul.

One day when Babel had gone to town, Tsires, at home in his flat, was stabbed to death with a Finnish dagger.

Babel returned to find the police in the house and the head of the criminal investigation department in his room. He sat at Babel's desk, writing his report. A polite young man in dark-blue riding breeches and top boots, he dreamed of becoming a writer and therefore treated Babel with respect.

'I must ask you to take your things and leave this house at once,' he said. 'Or I can't be responsible for your safety even for the next twenty-four hours. You know Moldavanka!'

So Babel fled, shuddering, pursued by Aunt Khava's wails and the curses she called down upon Simon Lop-Ear and all others whom she believed to be connected with the murder.

They were terrible curses. The polite policeman advised Babel:

'Don't listen to her ravings. She was in her right mind this morning and was able to give evidence. But now she's gone quiet mad. The ambulance from the asylum is coming for her in a moment.'

Beyond the partition, Aunt Khava steadily tore her hair, flung away the tufts, and screamed, sobbing and swaying to and fro:

'May you, Simon, get drunk on vodka with rat poison and die in your vomit! And may you kick your own mother Miriam, the old witch, for giving birth to such a fiend of hell! May all the Moldavanka boys sharpen their pen-knives and cut you into pieces during twenty days and twenty nights! May you, Simon, burn and burst in your own sizzling fat!'

Soon Babel learned everything there was to know about Tsires's death.

'Everything' was the fact that he had brought his fate upon himself. So not a living soul in Moldavanka pitied him, except Aunt Khava. He had proved to be dishonourable, and after that nothing in the world could save him from death.

This is what actually happened. The day before his death, Tsires called on Simon Lop-Ear.

Simon was shaving in the hall, in front of a magnificent cheval-glass in an ornate black frame.

He squinted at Tsires and said:

'Mixed yourself up with a nark, have you, Monsieur Tsires? Well, you know the new Soviet law – if you call on a man when he's shaving, state your business and buzz off. You're allowed twelve words, like at the central telegraph office. Any more, and your cut goes down by two hundred thousand a word.'

'Were you born with that unfortunate sense of humour?' Tsires asked with a sugary smile, 'or has it grown on you?'

Tsires was a coward in life and even in business, but, in his position of senior crib-spotter, he could afford to be cheeky in conversation.

'All right, you old clown,' said Lop-Ear, drawing his razor up and down through the air like a violin bow. 'Get on with it, before I run out of patience.'

'Four billion wage money,' said Tsires very softly, 'delivered tomorrow at one at the Concordia.'

'Right. You'll get your cut. No deductions this time.'

Tsires went home, but he wasn't altogether happy. He hadn't liked Lop-Ear's manner; it was too frivolous. Simon had never joked over a business deal before.

He confided in Aunt Khava, who turned on him at once:

'How long must you go on being such a fool? And don't look at Idochka's photograph, it's you I'm talking to, not her. Of course it's not a job for Simon. He'll never put himself out for a measly four billion. You'll have worked for nothing, that's all.'

'What am I to do then?' groaned Tsires. 'They'll drive me crazy, those bandits.'

'Go to Five Roubles. He might be tempted by your phoney billions. At least there's a chance, and you wont' look such a fool.'

So Tsires put on his lustrine cap and trudged off. Five Roubles lay asleep in the shadow of a white acacia in the cool of his garden. He heard Tsires out, and said drowsily:

'You'll get your cut.'

Tsires went off, delighted. He felt like a man who has just insured his life for pure gold. 'The old woman was right. You can't count on Lop-Ear. He's like a butterfly. Moody like a pregnant woman. What does it cost him to make a deal, and then play about with his razor and change his mind if it looks like too much trouble?'

But for the first and last time in his life, Tsires had blundered.

Next day, at one o'clock, Simon and Five Roubles met in front of the cash desk at the Concordia. They looked each other in the eye, and Simon asked:

'Would you mind telling me who tipped you off?'

'Old Tsires. And you?'

'Old Tsires.'

'So?'

I promise you Maupassant

'So old Tsires won't be with us much longer.'

'Amen,' said Five Roubles.

The two thieves parted amicably, keeping to the unwritten law that if two of them met on the same job, it was called off.

Forty minutes later, old Tsires was killed in his flat, while Aunt Khava was hanging the washing in the yard. She hadn't seen the murderer but knew it must be Simon or one of his men. Simon never forgave those who double-crossed him.

15
That Boy!

Living in Babel's house were Babel himself, his pretty, red-haired wife Evgenia, his quiet, austere mother, his sister Mary, and his mother-in-law who had come to stay with her small grandson.

One day in July a strange incident happened in the Babel household.

But I must first say something about Babel's marriage.

Babel's father, a bustling old man who kept a small agricultural machinery depot in Odessa, had been in the habit of sending his son Isaac to buy stock from a factory in Kiev. It belonged to the rich Kiev industrialist, Gronfein.

At Gronfein's, Babel met the daughter of the house, Evgenia, then in her last year at school, and they fell in love.

There could be no question of marriage: a penniless student, the son of a small Odessa tradesman, Babel was not a suitable match for Gronfein's heiress. The first time the subject was mentioned, Gronfein unbuttoned his frock-coat, stuffed his hands into the armholes of his waistcoat, and emitted the scornful sound 'Pshsh!' which speaks for itself. He didn't even bother to put his contempt into words – the wretched student wasn't worth it.

The young people saw there was only one way out – to flee to Odessa – and this they did.

The consequences followed the traditional pattern. Gronfein cursed the Babels to the tenth generation, and disinherited his daughter. It all went like in the famous poem by Sasha Cherny,[23] 'Love is not a potato', where, in similar circumstances, Papa

That Boy!

smashes the family dinner-service, Mama weeps into ten hand-kerchiefs, and the student – floridly described as 'the seducer of a maiden as pure as a poppy' – is driven from the house.

But time passed. Came the revolution. The Bolsheviks confiscated Gronfein's factory. The old man was reduced to going out unshaven, collarless and with a single gold stud in his shirt.

And then an astounding rumour reached the Gronfeins' ears: 'that boy' Babel had become an important writer, highly thought of and befriended by Maxim Gorky himself. (Just imagine, Maxim Gorky himself!) It was said that he received high royalties, and all who read him spoke respectfully of his 'great talent'. Some even added that little Genia had been very lucky to make such a brilliant match.

Clearly the old couple had slipped up, and the time had come to forgive and make friends. It hurt their pride, but they took the first step. Carrying the olive branch and excessively polite, Mrs Gronfein appeared unannounced at our Ninth Station.

Evidently feeling the need for support in her delicate mission, she had brought her eight-year-old grandson, Lucian, to ease the situation. She would have done better not to.

The Babels gave her a friendly welcome. But at the bottom of his heart Babel had inevitably retained a certain prejudice against his arrogant in-laws. Eager to make up for their past mistakes, Mrs Gronfein positively ingratiated herself with him, and stressed her warm regard for him at every step.

Izya and I often breakfasted with the Babels and witnessed the same scene repeated again and again.

Boiled eggs were served. Mrs Gronfein watched Babel like a hawk to see if he ate them and, if he didn't, asked in a hurt voice:

'Why don't you eat the eggs, Babel?' (She always called him by his surname.) 'Don't you like them?'

'Thank you, I don't want them.'

'Is that because you don't like your mother-in-law?' the old lady asked coyly, rolling her eyes. 'I cooked them specially for you.'

Babel choked over his breakfast and got up.

Izya nicknamed Lucian 'that boy'. The undertones of this southern term are impossible to convey. But the very day he arrived we all realised to our cost that Lucian was indeed 'that boy'.

From dawn till dusk Lucian's thin-lobed ears – red as though someone had been pulling them hard and enjoying it – were on fire with curiosity. Whatever was none of his business he ached to know. He spied on Babel and ourselves with fiendish vigilance. It was impossible to hide from him. Wherever we went, a minute later we could see, behind the foliage of a tamarisk or a rock on the beach, Lucian's ears translucent in the sun.

No doubt because he was eaten up by curiosity, he was unbelievably thin and bony. His eyes, black as olives, were everywhere at once, and he asked up to thirty questions a minute but never waited for an answer.

With his grasshopper temperament, he was a monstrously exhausting child. He was never quiet except when he was asleep. All day long he jerked, jumped, fidgeted, made faces, dropped and broke things, raced round the garden howling like a savage, swung on doors, fell down, laughed unnaturally, teased the dog, miaoued, tore his own hair out of spite, shook disgustingly with dry sobs if anyone crossed him, carried crabs and half-dead lizards with torn-off tails in his pockets and put them on the table in the middle of lunch, cadged, cheeked us, pinched my fishing rods and hooks and, to add to everything else, spoke in a grating voice.

'What's this?' he would ask. 'What's that for? Can you make dynamite out of a blanket? What happens if you drink tea with sand in it? Why have you got such a funny surname – Paustovsky – my Granny can never get it right till after dinner? Could you grab a tram from behind, with a hook, and stop it when it's going full speed, and pull it back? Why don't we make jam out of boiled crab?'

What we felt for the child can easily be imagined. Babel, his eyes flashing blue fire, called him 'that bat out of hell'.

Lucian's mere presence put him into such a state of nerves that he could do no work. He fled to our house and collapsed, groan-

ing. He called Lucian 'darling' in such a voice that, had the lop-
eared brat had an ounce of sense, his blood would have run
cold.

One hot day followed another. Mrs Gronfein showed no sign
of leaving, even in the distant future.

Babel clutched his head and moaned: 'I'm finished! Done for!
My head's buzzing like a brass boiler. As if that fiend were
bashing it all day with a stick!'

We all racked our brains to think of how to rid Babel of Lucian
and his Granny. In the end, as so often happens, he was saved by
an accident.

Early one morning I called for Babel to go swimming, as we had
arranged the night before.

He was writing at his desk. He looked hunted. As I opened the
door, he started and, without looking round, pushed his manuscript into the drawer so savagely that he nearly tore it.

'Oh, it's you!' he sighed when he saw me. 'I thought it was
Lucian. The only time I can work is before that monster wakes
up.'

Babel used indelible pencils. Pale and hard as nails, I hated
them. I said so. We began to argue and wasted the few vital
seconds before Lucian came sneaking up the corridor. If we
hadn't argued we might have got away in time.

We knew we were lost when Lucian burst triumphantly into the
room. He made a dash for Babel's desk and the drawer where he
believed the most interesting things were hidden, but Babel
forestalled him, locked the drawer and pocketed the key.

After that, Lucian picked up one thing from the desk after
another, asking what they were. Finally, he tried to snatch the
indelible pencil out of Babel's hand and, after a short struggle,
succeeded.

'I know what that is!' he shouted. 'It's a pencil-tensil for
scribbling-dibbling!'

Babel shuddered with disgust. I said to Lucian:

'That's an indelible pencil. Give it back to Isaac Emanuelovich
at once! D'you hear?'

'Indelible, incredible, inedible,' Lucian chanted, hopping on one foot and taking not the slightest notice of what I said.

'Oh, God!' moaned Babel. 'Let's go swimming. I can't stand much more of this.'

'I'll come with you,' Lucian cried. 'Granny said I could. Hunter's word. Shall I call her, and she'll tell you herself, Uncle Isaac?'

'No, no, no!' Babel sobbed in a tortured voice. 'No! Come on!'

We went to the beach. Lucian kept diving off the rocks, snorting and blowing bubbles. Babel watched him carefully, then caught hold of my hand and whispered:

'Do you know what I saw before we went out?'

'No.'

'He broke off the point of the indelible pencil and pushed it into his ear.'

'Does it matter?' I asked. 'It can't hurt him.'

'I suppose not,' Babel agreed glumly. 'Oh, to hell with him. Let him go on diving till he bursts.'

We began to talk about Herzen – Babel was re-reading him that summer. He tried to convince me that Herzen was a better writer than Tolstoy.

We were still arguing about it mildly on our way home, when Lucian ran ahead, turned to us and, pulling faces and dancing up and down, sang:

> *Herzen-Heffer fried in pepper,*
> *Fried in pepper Herzen-Heffer.*

'Will you,' said Babel at the end of his tether, 'hit that brat hard on the head, or I won't answer for myself?'

But Lucian must have heard him. He scuttled off to a safe distance and resumed his performance.

'Oo-oo-oo, the devil!' Babel muttered through clenched teeth. It was the first time I had heard his voice filled with such loathing. 'Another day of this, and I'll go off my head or hang myself.'

Fortunately, it didn't come to that. Half-way through breakfast, just as Mrs Gronfein was working up to her usual scene over the eggs ('Don't you like your mother-in-law, Babel?') Lucian clutched his ear, slipped off his chair, and rolled about the floor, shrieking in a heart-rending voice and kicking out at everything within reach.

We jumped to our feet. A dark and horrid discharge was pouring from his ear. He was screaming on a high-pitched, terrifying note, while the shouting women milled around him.

The whole house was in the grip of panic. Babel sat rigid, looking anxiously at Lucian who spun like a top, shrieking:

'It hurts! Oi! It hurts! Oi! It hurts!'

I tried to tell them that Lucian was lying – he was not in pain, he couldn't be. He had only been diving and got his ears full of water, and before we went out. . . .

But Babel nearly crushed my fingers under the table.

'Shut up!' he hissed. 'Not a word about the pencil. You'll ruin everything.'

His mother-in-law was sobbing, his sister Mary mopping up the purple fluid from Lucian's ear with cottonwool, his mother insisting that the child should go at once to a nose- throat- and ear-specialist in Odessa.

Babel rose, flung his napkin away, knocking over his half-full cup of tea and, red with anger at the incompetence of ignorant women, shouted:

'Are you mad, Mama? You'll kill that boy! Do you call them doctors in Odessa? They're vets! They're quacks, charlatans! Every man Jack of them, as you know perfectly well. They treat you for bronchitis and give you pneumonia. If they take a gnat out of your ear you'll end up with a perforated ear-drum.'

'Then what am I to do, oh Lord?' Mrs Gronfein cried, falling to her knees and flinging up her arms. 'Give me eyes that I may see. What am I to do?'

Lucian drummed with his heels on the floor and roared. But he was getting hoarse.

'You don't know?' Babel asked indignantly. 'You, a native of Kiev where you have a nose- throat- and ear-specialist who is world famous! Professor Grinfeld! The one person you can trust! My advice to you is: take the child to Kiev, at once!' He looked at his watch. 'There's a train in three hours. Mary, bandage up his ear. Tighter than that! Get his things on. I'll take you to the station and put you on the train. Don't worry about anything.'

They left in record time. As soon as they had gone, Evgenia burst out laughing and laughed until she cried. It dawned on me that the whole story of the 'world-famous professor' had been pure improvisation on Babel's part. He had carried it off like a born actor.

From that moment peace and quiet returned to our Ninth Station. Once again, we felt rational and human. And we regained our lost sense of the Odessa summer, brewing in the heat and the smell of seaweed.

A week later, a letter arrived from Kiev.

'Can you believe it?' Mrs Gronfein wrote indignantly. 'What do you think Professor Grinfeld found? Professor Grinfeld's verdict is that the little devil had stuffed a piece of indelible pencil into his ear! Apart from that there was not the slightest thing wrong with him! Not a thing! What do you think of that?'

16
Slave Labour

After the Lucian interlude we all went about at peace with the world, in that state of inner quiet that follows upon recovery from a severe illness or, as Izya said, when the soul has been purged by tragedy.

Babel got down to work. He always came out of his room silent and a little sad.

I too was writing, but very little. I was in a rare and pleasant mood. I described it myself as a mood of passionate observation of life. I had experienced it before but never so continuously and strongly.

Izya had finished his leave; he was back at *The Seaman,* and returned to Ninth Station only for the night. Sometimes he even slept in town. This suited me in a way. I would have felt too self-conscious in front of him to go on slowly, endlessly examining my surroundings, sometimes spending hours over a single detail, a thorny branch or a shell on the beach.

More than ever before, the smallest contact with the world around me filled me with joy.

The July days, a little yellow from the drought, merged into one, long, peaceful day. I often lay in the shifting shadow of the acacia in the garden, watching whatever I saw on the ground within the span of my arm.

Still more often, I walked to the far end of the beach, away from the houses, and swam about forty yards to a rock where I could lie all day in a hollow, sheltered from the sun, out of reach of the waves and hidden from the shore.

Years of Hope

I would take a book with me, but seldom read more than three or four pages a day. I fished for bullheads, or watched the ancient crab who often poked his head out from behind the rock and played hide and seek. As soon as our eyes met, he backed crossly into the thick, reddish seaweed that looked like branches of fir. But if I pretended not to see him, he raised his claw threateningly and sidled cautiously along, eyeing the carrots on the ground beside me (in those days our food was mainly carrots and tomatoes).

One day I was so busy reading that he managed to snatch one, fell with it into the water and sank like a stone. A moment later the carrot surfaced. The crab swam after it and tried to grab it, but I gave him a crack on the shell with my bamboo fishing rod and he scuttled away sideways to the bottom. I even thought he gave a cry of fright. Certainly he looked at me in terror, rolling his eyes.

The crab vanished, but a branch of flowering broom drifted close to the rock. I put my hand into the water to lift it out, and felt a shock. Although my hand was in the water, inches under the surface, I distinctly felt the sun warm on my palm.

I find it hard to convey the extraordinary impression of the heat of the sun, softened by the sea water, of sunshine touching my fingers while the greenish, buoyant water flowed between them.

It was a physical feeling which seemed close to happiness. I expected nothing better. It seemed unlikely that the surrounding world could give me anything more beautiful than this warm, friendly handclasp.

I fished out the broom, lay flat on the warm stone, and held the branch close to my eyes.

At Fountain the broom flowered all along the cliffs. But it grew with particular luxuriance at the foot of the garden walls, built of porous sandstone. The stone was friendly to the broom. The broom evidently liked heat, and hot streams of air sprang from the minute pores of the sandstone and created an area of warmth and shelter round the wall.

There, the broom took strong root and, like a large porcupine, shot the quills of its dark olive-green branches at the sky.

Slave Labour

The flowers, like bits of tender, compact sponge, absorbed at birth the golden colour of the sun.

They kept its brightness untarnished until late autumn. Then they slowly burnt themselves out on the cliffs, like rows of tiny lighthouses with golden beams you could see from far away.

Little by little I collected my facts. They all existed in the world outside but quickly turned into particles of my inner life.

Indeed, they did not for a moment exist independently. Immediately overgrown with images and particles of make-believe, they were like plants covered with fine dew-drops. You can no longer see the plant itself, although you recognise its shape.

I said this one evening to Babel.

We were sitting on the parapet on the cliff. Babel was absent-mindedly throwing pebbles into the sea; they cracked like pistol shots as they hit the rocks.

'It's all right for you other writers,' said Babel, although I was not yet a writer. 'You can wrap things up in the dew of your imagination, as you put it! What an awful expression, by the way! But what would you do if you had no imagination? Like me.'

'Rubbish!' I said angrily.

He seemed not to have heard me.

'Not one drop,' he repeated after a long pause and several pebbles. 'I'm quite serious. I can't make anything up. I have to know everything, down to the last wrinkle, or I can't even begin to write. "Authenticity", that's the motto, and I'm stuck with it! That's why I write so little and so slowly. Because it's terribly hard. So much for Mozart, the joy of creativity, the free flight of imagination! I wrote somewhere, I'm getting old from asthma, a mysterious disease I've had from birth and inherited together with my weak constitution. But that's a lie. What puts years on me is every single short-story I write. I work like a black, like a navvy, as if I had to dig up Everest with my own hands. When I start, I never believe I'll have the strength to finish. Sometimes I could weep, I'm so tired. It stops my circulation. If I get stuck over a sentence, it gives me spasms. And I'm always stuck over a sentence!'

'But your writing is so fluent,' I said. 'How do you do it?'

'That's style.' He gave a senile giggle in imitation of Moskvin.[24]
'Style! It's style that does it, young man, he-he-he! I'll write
about the weekly washing if you like, and the prose might sound
like Julius Caesar! That I seem to manage. But, you understand,
that's not the essence of art, it's the bricks, or the marble or the
bronze. Come, I'll show you how I do it. I'm a miser, a skinflint,
but just for you! . . .'

By now, it was dark inside the house. Beyond the garden the
sea rumbled more and more quietly with the approach of night.
Fresh air poured in from the sea and drove out the sultry wormwood smell of the steppe. Babel lit a small lamp. The light fell on
his glasses; behind them his eyes looked inflamed; he was always
having trouble with his eyes.

He got a thick wad of typescript out of his desk; there were at
least a hundred pages.

'Know what that is?'

I had no idea. Was it possible that Babel had at last written a
full length novella and kept it a secret from all of us? I could not
believe it. Babel, whose short stories were almost like telegrams!
Who packed everything into the smallest possible space. For
whom a story of ten pages was much too long and surely padded!

A hundred pages of his concentrated prose? No, it couldn't be!

I looked at the cover page, and saw the title 'Lyubka the
Cossack'. This was still more puzzling.

'Didn't I hear that "Lyubka the Cossack" is a very short short-
story that hasn't yet been published? Do you really mean you've
expanded it into a novella?'

He covered the typescript with his hand and laughed, his eyes
crinkling.

'It's "Lyubka" all right,' he said, blushing. 'And it's fifteen
pages long. But these are the twenty-two versions – two hundred
pages of it.'

'Twenty-two versions!'

'What's so terrible about that?' he bridled at once. 'Look here,
a work of art is not a pot-boiler. You write several versions of the

same story – so what? I'm not even sure the twenty-second is fit to publish. It looks as if it could still be tightened up. It's all this elimination that makes for power of language and style. Of language and style,' he repeated. 'You take anything – an anecdote, a bit of gossip – and you turn it into a story you yourself can't bear to put down. It glows like a jewel. It's round like a pebble. It hangs together by the cohesion of its parts. And its cohesion is so powerful that even lightning can't split it up. People will read it. And remember it. And they'll laugh over it, not because it's cheerful but because you always feel like laughing when somebody has brought something off. I have the nerve to talk about bringing it off only because we are alone. And you won't tell anyone about this conversation so long as I live. You must give me your word. It's no credit to me, of course. Goodness knows how someone like me, the son of a small broker, gets possessed by the demon or the angel of art. But whichever it is, I have to obey him like a slave, like a pack-mule. I've sold him my soul, and I have to write as well as I know how. It's my happiness, or my cross. More of a cross, I suppose. But take it away, and every drop of my blood will go with it and I won't be worth a chewed up fag-end. That's the work that makes a human being out of me and not just an Odessa street-corner philosopher.'

He paused, then went on more bitterly.

'I've got no imagination. All I've got is the longing for it. You remember Blok – "I see the enchanted shore, the enchanted distance." He got there all right, but I won't. I see that shore unbearably far off. I'm too sober. But I thank my lucky stars that at least I long for it. I work till I drop, I do all I can because I want to be at the feast of the gods and I'm afraid they'll throw me out.'

He took off his glasses, and wiped his eyes on the sleeve of his patched jacket.

'I didn't choose to be born a Jew,' he said suddenly. 'I think I can understand everything. Only not the reason for that black villainy they call anti-semitism.

'I came safely through a Jewish pogrom as a child, only they tore my pigeon's head off. Why? . . . I don't want Evgenia to come in,' he said softly. 'Put the door on the hook, will you? This kind of talk frightens her. She's liable to cry all night. She thinks I'm very lonely. Perhaps I am?'

What could I answer?

'So there it is,' said Babel, stooping short-sightedly over his manuscript. 'I work like a pack mule, but it's my own choice. I'm like a galley-slave who's chained for life to his oar but who loves the oar. Everything about it. Every grain of wood he's polished with his hands. If you use enough elbow grease, even the coarsest wood gets to look like ivory. That's what we have to do with words, and with our Russian language. Warm it and polish it with your hand, and it glows like a jewel.

'But I meant to tell you all I do, in the right order. The first version of a story is terrible. All in bits and pieces tied together with boring "link passages" as dry as old rope. You have the first version of "Lyubka" there – you can see for yourself. It yaps at you, it's clumsy, helpless, toothless.

'That's where the real work begins. I go over each sentence, time and again. I start by cutting all the words it can do without. You have to keep your eye on the job because words are very sly, the rubbishy ones go into hiding and you have to dig them out – repetitions, synonyms, things that simply don't mean anything.

'After that, I type the story and I let it lie for two or three days. If I can hold out. Then I check it again, sentence by sentence and word by word. And again I find a lot of rubbish I missed the first time. So I make another copy, and another – as many as I have to, until I've cleaned it all up and there's not a speck of dirt left.

'But that's not all! When I've done the cleaning up, I go over every image, metaphor, comparison, to see if they are fresh and accurate. If you can't find the right adjective for a noun, leave it alone. Let the noun stand by itself.

'A comparison must be as accurate as a slide rule, and as natural as the smell of fennel. Oh, I forgot – before I take out the rubbish, I break up the text into shorter sentences. The more full stops the better. I'd like to have that passed as a law. Not more than one idea and one image to one sentence. Never be afraid of full stops.

Slave Labour

Actually, my own sentences are too short – that's because of my asthma. I can't talk for long. The longer the sentence the more I get short of breath.

'I take out all the participles and adverbs I can. Participles are heavy, angular, they destroy the rhythm. They grate like tanks going over rubble. Three participles to one sentence, and you kill the language. All that "presenting", "obtaining", "concentrating" and so on. . . . Adverbs are lighter. They can even lend you wings in a way. But too many of them make the language spineless, it starts mioaling. . . . A noun needs only one adjective, the choicest. Only a genius can afford two adjectives to one noun.

'The breaking up into paragraphs and the punctuation have to be done properly but only for the effect on the reader. A set of dead rules is no good. A new paragraph is a wonderful thing. It lets you quietly change the rhythm, and it can be like a flash of lightning that shows the same landscape from a different aspect. There are writers, even good ones, who scatter paragraphs and punctuation marks all over the place. They can write good prose, but it has an air of muddle and carelessness because of this. Even Kuprin used to do that.

'Line is as important in prose as in an engraving. It has to be clear and hard.

'My twenty-two versions of "Lyubka" gave you a shock. They are all part of the weeding, sifting, pulling the story out into a single thread. There can be as much difference between the first and last version of a book as between a greasy bit of packing paper and Boticelli's "Spring".'

'It really is slave labour,' I said. 'A man should think twenty times before he decides to become a writer.'

'But the most important thing of all,' said Babel, 'is not to kill the story by working on it. Or else all your labour has been in vain. It's like walking a tight-rope. Well, there it is. . . . We ought all to take an oath not to mess up our job.'

I went home, but I was awake all night. I lay on the verandah and looked at some lilac-coloured planet that had tunnelled the immeasurable spaces of the sky with its delicate light and was flashing signals, trying to approach the earth, but without success.

The night was huge, its darkness made it boundless. I knew that on such nights the sea had a dull sheen and, somewhere far beyond the horizon, the tops of the mountains shone with reflected light. They were cooling down. It was a pity they gave back their daylight warmth to cosmic space. Our verbena could have done with it. It held its petals clasped like hands over its face to keep it from the cold before the dawn.

In the morning, Izya Livshitz came over from Odessa. He usually arrived in the evening so I was surprised by this early visit.

Avoiding my eyes, he told me that four days ago, on the 7th of August, Alexander Blok had died in Petrograd.

Izya turned away, cleared his throat and said:

'Will you go and tell Babel? . . . I can't.'

I felt my heart thumping against my ribs and the blood draining from my head. All the same I went.

Teaspoons tinkled peacefully on the verandah.

I stood for a few moments at the gate, heard Babel laugh at something and, hiding behind the garden wall not to be seen from the verandah, went home to our dilapidated house. I too could not bring myself to tell Babel that Blok had died.

17
Near and Far

I saw you go down into the narrow dwelling
where there are not even dreams. And
still I cannot believe it.

DELACROIX

The weather was very still. At the foot of the red Sarmatian clay
the sea lay molten and heavy. The shore had the sharp, dusty smell
of long-ripe goosefoot shedding its seeds. Izya Livshitz quoted
Blok:

The silence of the dying grain –
A time of radiance in the world.

We talked endlessly about Blok. One evening Bagritsky came
from Odessa, and recited Blok nearly all night through. Izya and
I were silent. We lay on the dark verandah. The night wind
crackled in the dry vine leaves.

Bagritsky sat, cross-legged like a Turk, on an old mattress
worn flat as a pancake. He was starting an attack of asthma. He
gasped, and smoked asmatol, a greenish powder that smells like
burnt hay, and breathed with such difficulty that he seemed to
suck the air through a straw. It wheezed, gurgled and rattled in his
chest.

He was not supposed to talk during an attack. But he wanted to
recite Blok all the same, and we didn't try to dissuade him.

For a long time he sat muttering, trying to calm himself: 'Just a
minute. It won't be long now. Only don't talk to me.' In the end

he began to recite without waiting for the attack to pass, and something like a miracle happened: apparently soothed by the rhythm of the verse, his breathing quietened, and his strong, beautiful voice rang out more and more clearly.

He recited the best-known poems, and we were grateful for it.

> *A thick and heavy curtain at the entrance,*
> *Beyond the window – night and mist. . . .*
> *What of the freedom, hateful to you now,*
> *Don Juan, who have learned to fear?*

Both the poem and Bagritsky's voice seemed to me, for some reason, so irreparably tragic that I felt like weeping.

Again there was silence, and the darkness broken only by the unintelligible signalling of the stars. Then again the grave music of a familiar poem:

> *Already in my heart I know you. The years go by,*
> *And still the image lingers. . . .*

So the night passed. Bagritsky recited, almost sang the 'Verses about Russia', *The Scythians*, Ravenna 'sleeping in sleepy eternity's arms'. It was almost dawn before he fell asleep. He slept sitting up, leaning against the wall of the verandah, and groaned in his deeply exhausting sleep.

His face was drawn, wizened; a crust, as of dry wormwood juice, had formed on his blue-white lips, and he looked like an enormous, tousled bird.

I was to remember that white crust on Bagritsky's lips several years later, in Moscow. I was following his coffin. Behind us, the hooves of a cavalry squadron clicked on the cobbles.

Ill and breathless, Samuel Marshak[25] walked beside me, leaning trustfully on my still-young shoulder, and saying:

'You remember? "By hooves and stones . . . the years are tried. . . . Immortal wormwood . . . impregnates the waters – and its bitterness . . . is on our lips." How . . . magnificent!'

A dusty sky hung over dingy, sultry Yakimovka. Children shouted, playing 'I spy' in the back-yards. The band struck up a muted funeral march, and the cavalry horses, obedient to the music, took slower steps.

Near and Far

But on that far-away morning in 1921, Bagritsky left by the first tram, without even having tea, and without calling on Babel. He was feeling ill. He coughed, his breath wheezed, and he hardly spoke. Evidently he had overtaxed his lungs the night before.

Izya and I took him to the tram, and went to see Babel. As usual in times of trouble, we needed company.

Babel was writing in his room. He pushed his manuscript aside, and placed a large grey pebble over it.

Occasionally a soft breeze from the sea blew in, and everything light and mobile in the room – window curtains, papers, the flowers in a tumbler – fluttered like a small bird in a snare.

'What shall we do now?' Babel said sadly. 'We won't see another Blok if we live to be two hundred.'

'Did you ever see him?' I asked.

I waited for him to say no, and relieve my mind. I am not often envious, but for a long time I was bitterly to envy all who had seen and heard Blok.

'I did, yes,' said Babel. 'I even went to his flat at the corner of Pryazhka and Officer Street.'

'What was he like?'

'Not at all as you imagine.'

'How do you know what I think of him?'

'Because it's sure to be what I thought of him myself. Until I saw him. He was not at all like a fallen angel. Nor was he the embodiment of exquisite feelings and thoughts. He was a reserved, middle-aged man, strong, though tired. He had very good manners, so he didn't burden you with his gloom or his learning. First we sat in the dining-room on two, facing, bent-wood chairs. The kind of chairs that bore you at sight. It was a depressing room, anything but the hall of the shining knight in the white mask. And his study didn't smell of Nile lilies and intoxicating ladies in black silk. It smelt of dust and books. An ordinary flat in an ordinary house. Now you look disgusted! You don't like what I'm telling you, and you'll go away saying I'm a sceptic, a cynic, with no fire in my heart. I see only the grey undercoat that shows through the marvellous colours, I don't even know the colours are there. But that's just your romantic schoolboy non-sense. The beauty of a spirit like Blok can do without a gilt frame. And without organ peals or incense. Blok was by nature a prophet. He even had the prophet's hard look in his eyes. He saw the doom of the old world. The seeds of destruction were already coming up. But the night dragged on, and it seemed as though it would never end. So he welcomed even the cheerless, harsh light of the new, revolutionary dawn as a deliverance. He took the revolution into his poet's world and he wrote *The Twelve*. He really was a prophet, of course. Both in his visions and in that shattering music he heard in the sound of Russian speech.

'He could transpose what he saw from one plane to another; and there it developed unexpected qualities for half-blind people like us. You and I see flowers – roses, say – in summer, in gardens or squares. But that wasn't enough for him. He wanted to set new, unheard-of roses alight on earth. And he did:

And roses, autumn roses
I dream at every step
Through mist and fire and frost
On the light, white snow.

You wish you had seen Blok. Naturally! But if I had an ounce of imagination, I would try to see, in every possible concrete detail, what exactly Blok was saying, if only in those four lines. Picture it to myself clearly, accurately – and then the world would reveal to me one of its hidden and remarkable facets, and, living and singing in that world, this extraordinary man, such as are born once in a century. He takes us by the hand – insignificant people, crippled by our "properly run" lives – and leads us to those dunes over a northern sea where, you remember, "the sunset turns the sky into a deep and many-coloured chalice" and "dusk holds hands with dawn". And where the air is so clear that a distant, red buoy – an ordinary, roughly made object – "glows in the dusk like the jewel of the Belle Ferronière."'

Babel had an extraordinary memory, he was always quoting poetry by heart and hardly ever made a mistake.

'There it is,' he said after a moment. 'Blok knew the ways into the kingdom of beauty. He was a giant, of course, he towers above everyone. The only one who rings in the heart as splendidly as a thousand harps. But most people think it matters that he had bentwood chairs in his dining-room, and that he was "Zemhussar"[26] in the World War. They like that. Any smelly little flame of ignorant gossip and prejudice will bring them running.'

It was the first time I heard Babel use a comparison like the 'ringing of a thousand harps'. He was severe, even self-conscious in his choice of words in conversation. Anything in the way of flourish or glitter made him blush and frown with distaste. Perhaps because of this, any words of the 'high flown' sort he used, sounded natural and rang true, coming from his lips. But he used them very seldom indeed, and always pulled up at once and began jeering at himself. This could be extremely irritating. Izya, for one, could never stand Babel in this mood of almost cynical self-mockery. Nor could I, and my own clashes with Babel – admittedly fairly rare – all arose over his savage debunking of himself, and putting on cynical airs.

But he didn't debunk his 'thousand harps' and, from the way he spoke, I thought he probably read Blok to himself at night, when he was alone and shed his disguise.

I was later convinced of this by Bagritsky, who was fond of quoting other people's sayings and did it with the simplicity of a child. One day, when we were talking about Blok, he coughed and began a little uncertainly:

'You understand – nothing but harps and the muted voice of the poet. Blok's voice was like that. I could recite all his poems to the sound of harps, and each one differently. Honestly! I would draw out the music from each verse, like a golden thread from a tangled skein. And people would listen, and forget time, and life and death, and the movement of the stars and the beating of their own hearts. There's some sensitive young German scribbler, I forget his name – as a poet he's a bit subject to colds in the head, but he wrote one thing that wasn't bad. It was about there being beautiful sounds locked up in every human word. But these sounds submit only to the will of great poets and musicians. Only they can release them from captivity inside the words.'

'Eddie!' said Izya. 'Stop repeating Babel's words and twisting them. This is a horrible hotch-potch of what he says.'

'It's what I think myself,' Bagritsky replied modestly.

'Really? And since when have you become so eloquent?'

'That's enough!' Bagritsky snapped. 'I'm sick of sarcastic schoolboys with the brains of white mice. Why can't you leave me in peace, for goodness sake? Why are you all running after me, trying to prove to me I'm not as clever as you would like to think?'

I managed to stop the quarrel, but Bagritsky grumbled on for a long time about 'imported infant prodigies' and 'intellectual renegades'.

He was hurt because, instead of being charmed by the fascinating subject he had brought up, Izya had butted in like the spoil-sport devil in the fairy tale.

Any show of disrespect for poetry wounded Bagritsky to the quick, and could even lead to violence.

In general, apart from Babel and some women poets, young Odessa poets and writers were inclined to be very quarrelsome. Literary arguments, even on such abstract themes as regular and irregular metres in verse, were apt to end in personal insults if not actual blows.

18
A Fight in a Good Cause

Posters the colour of watery tomato soup appeared on the walls. They announced a fabulous poetry evening shortly to be held in some dilapidated hall in Pushkin Street; all the poets of Odessa were to take part.

Printed in bold type across the poster was the further announcement:

AT THE END OF THE EVENING
THE POET SHENGELI WILL BE BEATEN UP

Underneath, someone had added in ink:

'If he dares to come.'

The tickets were expensive. They sold out within three hours.

Izya Livshitz thought the beating up had been announced with the knowledge and consent of Shengeli.

The poet George Shengeli was a good-natured man of exotic appearance. I could never understand why many of the local poets seemed to dislike him. I asked Bagritsky, but he was evasive. In the end I assumed that baiting Shengeli was a form of literary sport. It added to the zest of life in Odessa's poetic circles.

Shengeli seemed to me to enter into the spirit and to put on his air of Roman stoicism as part of the game.

During his clashes with the poets, his clean-cut face grew pale and looked like a marble carving. As such, it would have been an ornament to the Roman Forum, Izya said – 'Or perhaps to the Pantheon?' he added with a worried frown.

Shengeli was tall, his eyes had retained the sparkle of youth. He went about Odessa barefoot, in a tropical pith helmet. For the rest, he was widely cultured, wrote sophisticated verse, translated French poets and was well-disposed towards his fellow-men, and well mannered.

All this annoyed many local poets – brash young men who prided themselves on their freedom from affectation and above all from the mortal sins of too much education and forebearance.

I had seen Shengeli for the first time in Moscow, at the beginning of the war. He was taking part in one of Igor Severyanin's[27] recitals and reading his own poems in the intervals. They were poems about his native, stony Kerch, an ancient land where 'Scythians, Sarmatians, Huns and Vends sleep in the desert soil', and where 'ageless legends haunt the minds of men'.

He said about himself:

> *I breathe with the breath of the tides*
> *And, as of old, my blood*
> *Is warmed by the same warmth*
> *As the southern sea. . . .*

I have always felt that I could as easily be carried away by certain other occupations as I am by writing – sailing, for instance, or archaeology, or the further exploration of countries long ago discovered.

Archaeology is the study of antiquity, and ever since my childhood antiquity had meant to me the wind racing over the feathergrass, in ancient, lonely sun-baked lands, to which it brings a hint of freshness from the near-by coast, or a broken tile made by the thin grey fingers of an Iranian potter, or a black clay pipe shaped like the bow of an Achaean ship and lost by some Dnieper Cossack near the salt lakes of Perekop. I was fascinated by the colour of these ancient lands – harsh, rusty, mineral.

That was how I always pictured to myself the ancient regions of the earth. When I actually saw them I was pleasantly surprised to find that the colours that bear witness to the fabulous age of the earth are many more than I had supposed.

I was finally convinced of this in the Aegian Islands, Greece and Italy. There, the rusty earth showed in the distance through the indigo air of morning or the majestic, dull copper of dusk. Antiquity wore many colours and many tones, combining crimson rocks and olive foliage, or the dark gold of sunset with the lilac air of an Ionian evening.

The strong, hard colours of antiquity belong to the south rather than to the north. There they are more noticeable, you see them more often.

From a hotel window in Rome you can look at a fresh lawn being sprinkled with artificial rain from nickel-plated pipes and, almost next to it, see the ancient, ageless soil of the arena of the Coliseum.

It looks as old as the sky over Rome, over the near-by Appenines, over Calabria burnt to a heap of cement dust.

Calabria smokes with heat like a huge fire on a still day. Her coast smells of flint from which a spark has just been struck. Were it not for the dense, cool, violet sea washing this dry land, the sight of it would make you shudder like the threshold of hell.

The sense of antiquity is also the sense of the infinite flight of time, a sense of history, and of the future.

For some reason this sense of time is always sharper near the sea.

I have digressed from my story, and I might as well digress a little further and say something of what the sense of being by the sea means to me.

You can look at the sea from the deck of an ocean liner or of a fishing barge.

From the low deck of a barge you not only see it but you smell the tang of sea-water as the boat passes submerged rocks. For an instant they are laid bare by a wave and reveal their thick coats of shaggy seaweed.

And in that moment, between one wave and the next, the seaweed gives out a sharp smell, and you can fill your lungs with it to the point of giddiness.

You never smell the sea from the high deck of a liner. All you smell are hot engine oil, cigarette smoke, and lavatory deodorants.

You really get the feel of the sea only in places where its smells have been brought out by pure and prolonged heat. They hardly exist in Yalta, for instance. The surf smells of sodden cigarette ends and orange peel, not of scorching hot breakwaters, old rope, savory, washed up mines of 1912 vintage, harbour timbers grey with salt, or pink fishing nets.

This is the sea you smell only in ports like Kerch, Novorossisk, Feodosia, Mariupol or Skadovsk.

There are seaside resorts built over with blue ice-cream kiosks, cluttered up with plaster statues of boy and girl athletes, teeming with skull-caps, sandals, turkish towels and striped pyjamas. And there are shores burnt by millenia of sunlight reflected from huge southern seas, and hot currents of the cleanest air in the world.

This sun and air give them their harsh colour – ochre, rusty, greyish, like cinders – the colour of time out of mind, of eternity. And from century to century the countless, measured waves break over their bare, petrified clay.

The real sea has many different smells, colours and sounds. If I had the time, and were not so nervous about upsetting the balance of my book, I would expand this digression to the size of a volume.

I must admit, I can be perfectly happy reading a guide-book on Greece, Botkin's *Letters from Spain* or the *Diaries* of Miklukho-Maklaï, and equally happy pouring the sand through my fingers and resting with the whole of my being, while the wind pats my cheeks with its cool damp hands. It seems to be pleased that there is not another soul on the beach, all the way to the horizon where the bluish promontories look like a company of bears lapping the sea-water.

All day long the stiff grass rustles on the cliffs. Infinitely old, this gentle sound, heard on this shore for century after century, imparts the love of wisdom and simplicity.

On the night of the party, Izya, Yasha Lifshitz and I managed with difficulty to get into the hall, where the poet Chicherin was reciting amidst a frenzied din of laughter and catcalls.

The noise died down a little when a man with a withered arm and a clever taut face followed him on to the stage. I had never seen Vladimir Narbut before, though I had long admired his poetry.

A Fight in a Good Cause

Paying no attention to the turmoil, he began to recite in a cold, menacing voice with a slight Ukrainian accent:

And I, a rotting log
A coffin weathered by the years. . . .

There was something sinister about his poems, although at times a moving tenderness broke into the lines:

It is of you, of you, of you
I want to speak in sleepless verse. . . .

Gradually, the audience grew silent.

The stage was packed to bursting with young men and girls, Valentin Katayev among them, noticeable by his bright red fez. The platform creaked, swayed and looked ready to collapse at any minute.

'Can they really all be poets?' asked Yasha, who had a habit of asking naive questions. 'There are enough of them to fill a whole country in Central Europe.'

Shengeli sat on a kitchen stool at the foot of the platform, his topee on his knees. So might a bronzed legionary, finding himself in the Senate, have held his battle-scarred helmet.

'Thank goodness he's come,' Izya sighed with relief. 'Now we can be sure of a row.'

Hoarse and sulky, Katayev read a poem about blind fish. Fishermen from Sanzheyka and Great Fountain sometimes caught blind fish from the Danube: they had been blinded by the change from fresh water to salt. The poem was well received but not given an ovation. The audience was looking forward to the row and saving its strength.

Kirsanov,[28] still a beardless boy, noisy and quarrelsome, kept jumping up from his chair and shouting provocatively at Shengeli. But Shengeli looked unmoved and this evidently angered Kirsanov who jumped up again to shout something still more insulting.

Each time he got up a sleepy-looking boy who sat behind him pulled him back by his coat tails; the coat was cracking at the seams. Kirsanov swore and sat down, but bobbed up again at once.

A few other young men joined in the shouting.

But the row was plainly not getting under way. The audience grew restive.

'Why are they so excited, these poets?' asked Yasha. 'You'd think they're electing the Poet Laureate, or awarding the Nobel Prize. What are they trying to do?'

Izya, who knew, said nothing.

Then a number of things happened which confused the audience completely.

An unknown actress with a baying voice began to recite Myrra Lokhvitskaya. This was a mistake. It provoked a disapproving growl which soon turned into an angry roar:

'To hell with doggerel! To hell with Myrra! Better give us "The Night breathed Lust and Passion"!'

The actress, a dappled blonde with arms like withered branches, clutched at the table for support and broke into theatrical sobs.

Shengeli rose, on fire with old-world chivalry. The mob of poets and their dishevelled girl-friends had dared insult an innocent woman! Shame! He shouted a few insults at the crowd.

Then Bagritsky jumped up. I was sure he was going to set upon and rend his enemy Shengeli, but he turned instead to the audience at large and made a violent gesture as though to deal a knock-out blow to all. He swung his right arm, shrieked, fainted, and crashed to the floor.

The hall was in an uproar. No one could make out what was happening. Medical aid was summoned. His face stony, Narbut closed the meeting.

Human eddies of arguing, spluttering, yelling boys and girls milled around the exits. Insults and encouragements flew like tennis balls across the hall.

Ambulance attendants pushed through the crowd and led away Bagritsky, conscious but white with pain. 'I think I've broken my shoulder,' he said to us with a tight smile. 'Or dislocated it perhaps. . . . What bloody fools! Couldn't even start a proper row!'

The ambulance drove off. Yasha and I broke through the serried ranks of poets and their disciples, and came out into the open air and quiet of Pushkin Street.

A Fight in a Good Cause

'What on earth was all that meant to be?' Yasha asked again. 'Bedlam, or a drunken brawl? Or just a boyish prank? And at such a time! It's too silly.'

Yasha was furious. We saw Izya and joined him. He looked dejected.

'Well, that was a flop,' he said. 'They ought never to have started that nonsense – boasting they would actually beat up Shengeli. Lucky for us people didn't ask for their money back.'

'But what was it all about?' I asked.

It was then he told us that the party had been held in aid of the Homeless Children's Fund. There was a special commission in charge of the fund. Its delegate had made the arrangements with a group of poets. To make sure of a full house, they had decided they must have a sensational attraction. They racked their brains for a long time; finally someone came up with the idea of beating up Shengeli. This was welcomed as novel and original. For the sake of the cause, Shengeli readily agreed.

The plan had failed because too few people had been taken into the organisers' confidence. But since all the tickets had been sold, the delegate was delighted. He even planned a repeat performance.

A Casino was opened in Havana Street, all the takings to go to the Fund. The game was *petits chevaux*, a form of roulette.

I went one evening with Torelli. Tobacco smoke hung in the air like stratus cloud. Cigarette butts soaked in the dregs of beer at the bottom of dirty glasses. Pale young men in naval caps gambled furiously in silence.

The croupier, an old man with an English parting in his thin hair, rattled on in a tinny voice like a wound-up toy.

'*Les jeux sont faits.* No more stakes. Citizen, will you please remove your hand from the table. Yes, it's in my way. Remove it at once. Before it's too late. And kindly refrain from using obscene language. This is a government institution, not a brothel. Citizen players! I'll stop the game unless that thief goes. Either you talk to him or I call the police. Finished! No more play. Take your stakes back. The Casino is closed!'

Then some brawny lad in a check cap and shaggy muffler, a

cigarette between his lips, would go up to the thief, silently grab him by the shirt front, pull him off his chair (the chair invariably crashed to the floor), propel him at arm's length to the door and throw him out. Each time the door bell, which had survived from pre-revolutionary times, gave a frightened jingle. The only other sound throughout the scene was that of the brawny lad and the thief breathing heavily through the nose.

The lad returned to the table and the croupier said:

'Well done, young man, *merci beaucoup*. The game continues. Raise your stakes, citizens! The longer you think about it, the more you put off your lady luck!'

The thief stood on the pavement, clutched the clients by the sleeve as they went in, and addressed them earnestly:

'Be my witness, young man, I'll fix that spotty-faced croupier and that bastard from the water-melon dock if it's the last thing I do. Spit in my eye if I don't. Where are you off to! Oh, you're in a hurry? Well, I humbly ask you to wait a minute just the same.'

Unbuttoning his coat, he thrust his mighty, heaving chest at the client, and whined drunkenly:

'At least give me five thousand. I'll turn it into a million. You'll take half. Don't drive a man to desperation.'

He was hard to shake off, and most people gave him something, as did Torelli and I. We lost the rest of our money on a single throw, whereupon the croupier, frowning at the foul smoke from his cigarette, said coldly:

'No stakes? You'll have to do better than that, boys.'

We left, offended. Later, I returned several times, but never again to gamble. I watched the croupier. I was hypnotised by his mixture of insolence, politeness, utter scorn for everyone and incredible rudeness. I wondered what he had been in the past. He turned out to be a former opera singer: Torelli had actually heard him in the role of Mephistopheles.

19

Time Slows Down

In August I decided to spend my leave from *The Seaman* in Ovidiopol.

A lethargic little town, lost in the steppe on the shores of the Dniester estuary, it was reputed to be the place of exile and death of the poet Ovid.

In fact, Ovid died in a Roman convict settlement much further south, near the mouth of the Danube. Before his death he wrote complaining of the Scythian cold and the gloomy, turbulent Black Sea.

I could never understand why the Black Sea had struck him as gloomy. I had always thought of it as one of the brightest and gayest of seas. And how could anyone speak of Scythian cold in a region where it doesn't even snow every winter, and when the snow does come it stays only a few days and leaves the thawed-out earth smelling faintly of spring?

That autumn of 1921 was dry and burnt to its very core. The trouble about walking to Ovidiopol was not so much the heat as the churning dust. It rushed in whirling pillars along the dirt-tracks, turned everyone as brown as a Kafir, and was impossible to wash off.

So, instead of going to the estuary, I decided to follow the sea-shore, past the deserted Fountains to the last tram stop. The stop was known as Kovalevsky's Dacha. As I dislike travelling blind, I got a book called *Old Odessa* and read up everything it had to say of Kovalevsky and his *dacha*.

Years of Hope

I learned that Kovalevsky had been a rich and lonely Odessan who bought a dry strip of coastal steppe; there he built himself a house by the sea and, next to it, a tall round tower like a lighthouse. The tower had no function. He built it, as children say, 'just like that', to please himself. He climbed it a few times, had tea on the top landing, and ended by jumping off it and crashing to his death.

The house quickly turned into a ruin. A clumsy, gloomy building, no one wanted to live in it. But the tower remained and was mentioned in all the Black Sea navigation manuals. It seems that it was an important landmark on the way to Odessa, so it was preserved and people were forbidden to pull it down for the stones.

I knew that several houses stood empty nearby and I decided to stay in whichever of them I liked best.

I walked from Odessa, taking my time over the journey. I set out from Black Sea Street at first light.

Although nothing happened on the way, every detail of the road imprinted itself on my memory so that afterwards I could at any moment retrace it in my mind, step by step.

In later years I went over that road again and again, always on foot, although by then, not only buses and trams were running but even taxis were raising the dust.

The whole charm of the way, its compelling fascination for me, lay in its nearness to the sea. At no point were the cliffs too far away for me to hear the waves and smell the seaweed.

I had only to bend down and pick up a white stone and blow off the dust, to know that here, hot from the midday sun, was a grained pebble from the bottom of the sea, and to wish I knew the history of that piece of stone over all its thousands of years.

Everything along the road smelt of sea and sun – even the kiosks where, once upon a time, cider had been sold. The cracking paint peeled off in diamond-shaped flakes and smelt of the heat of the sun. The empty zinc counters were green with the pollen of goosefoot and wild wormwood, and the same pollen gave a greenish tinge to the whole surface of the road.

The walls – they looked as though they were built of petrified sponge – smelt of the sea. Countless minute shells were encrusted in the stones, scratchy and glittering like chipped mother-of-pearl.

In places the thick dust on the road was marked by a fisherman's net which had been dragged across it at dawn. The net had laid the dust and left clumps of rough seaweed and tiny fish which by now were dry and looked like tinsel cut-outs. The clumps of seaweed, wet and hot inside, smelt of brine and steamed.

Lizards ran about the orange Marseilles tiles on the roofs. I imagined that the making of these tiles (they must have come from somewhere in the south of France, near Marseilles or Toulon) was a leisurely craft which had kept some of its ancient secrets and had therefore a certain aura of romance. I was sure that all the Marseilles tile factories stood near the sea.

I wished I could study the manufacturing process and write a short book about it. I don't know how much useful information the reader would have gained from it, but I would certainly have tried to infect him with my feeling for the poetry of making tiles.

I also liked these tiles because they were connected with the south and the sea: looking from the window of the Moscow–Odessa train, I had only to catch sight of red-tiled roofs in the glassy distance to know that the sea could not be far off.

The tides were always washing up polished fragments of tiles on the beach and I never tired of admiring their rich carroty colour and finely grained texture.

Here and there in Great Fountain dusty bunches of grapes hung in the small gardens of fishermen's huts. The long grapes smelt of nutmeg and shone with pink juice against the light. I got a large bunch in exchange for three fills of tobacco.

Beyond Great Fountain the road turned off into the steppe. The houses stayed behind, shy of the blinding heat. On either side of the highway rustled weightless leaves of maize. The cobs had all been picked. However hard I looked I could not find one that had been missed.

The cicadas sang their subterranean song, the heat flowed like a river, at intervals all the dry maize stalks crackled softly. I was glad of the sound – it meant that a cool breeze, however faint, was blowing from the sea.

Years of Hope

These are only some of the things I saw and thought about on my way to Kovalevsky's tower. And always the sea was beside me, playing like molten lapis-lazuli – the splendid sea, an abyss of coolness and soothing sound.

I reached Kovalevsky's tower when the heat was beginning to abate. Several houses surrounded by gardens stood on the cliffs. All the doors and windows were broken, and the gardens overgrown with tall dry weeds.

The one I chose had a timbered turret. A spiral staircase led to the top. It was undamaged. By some miracle, so were the balcony door and the glass of the only window in the tower room. Most important of all, the floor boards were intact.

The *dacha* was one of five, all uninhabited save by grey lizards and swallows.

I decided to settle down in the tower room. I felt as though I were in a lighthouse.

Rarely have I experienced such complete freedom, such a sense of being on my own to live as I please, of being at once a Robinson Crusoe and a hermit, the master of my time and of all the days to come. As for the everyday tasks and domestic chores that people usually find a burden, to me they seemed a light and even pleasant occupation.

I broke up dry wormwood and made a splendid big besom for sweeping the house.

Before dark I went down to the beach and gathered armfuls of dry, soft, matted seaweed, making sure that it was properly weathered and had lost its medicinal smell. It made excellent bedding for sleeping on the floor.

It is well known that, the fewer possessions a man has, the dearer they are to him, the more closely bound up with his life and the more important to him in all circumstances.

I unpacked my rucksack. With a feeling of thankfulness I took out my wick-lamp and a small bottle of spirit, two packets of tobacco, rusks, groats, saccharine, tea made of grated carrots, coarse red salt and a few other foodstuffs. At the bottom of the sack were a sailor's vest, an exercise book, a bottle of ink made from indelible pencil, and several books. Anything else I would have to find on the spot, in the sea or the steppe.

I had also brought fishing lines and a large supply of silvered hooks. Odessa fishermen believed that sea fish take silvered hooks in preference to bronze or black. Personally, I thought this was sheer prejudice but, at the Sixteenth Station fishing village, it had enabled me to barter hooks for a large bottle of cloudy sunflower oil; ever since I had felt like Croesus.

I spent my first night in a restless but pleasant state between sleep and wakefulness. I slept, and yet I clearly heard the waves, the cicadas, the shuffling of the sand on the dunes and the soft creaking of an old electric wire which swung day and night from a post near the iron gate.

Sometimes all the sounds ceased abruptly and, after a few moments, a sigh came from the steppe as though some huge beast had settled down more comfortably to sleep.

I closed my eyes and when I opened them again a moment later a shadowy blue light filled the room up to the ceiling. It was the same colour as the sky beyond the window – I could see it as a great, smooth, hazy abyss. Crimson banks of cloud were forming in its blue. It must have been close on dawn but this did not at once occur to me and I continued to doze, waking every ten minutes or so, every time surprised to see the room emerging, as on a photographic print, in ever clearer and sharper detail out of the gloom.

Morning finally came when a small bird settled on the balcony rail and cheeped:

'Wasps sleep, wasps sleep, wasps sleep, don't sleep!'

'Don't sleep, don't sleep!' he repeated insistently, and the yellow tuft on his head lit up like a feathered flame in the first rays of the sun.

The sun, as it rose over the enormous spaces of the earth, looked much too large to shed its first light upon the single tiny wool-tuft of a crest on the head of a small bird.

I got up and went down to the sea to bathe. The cliffs were dangerously steep, in places almost sheer.

Years of Hope

Later on I climbed through the trap in the verandah floor and underneath found a rusty spade and many other highly necessary things – a hammer, a pile of bent nails, a coil of wire and a large tin labelled 'Monpensier-Landrin'.

All these things I took and found very handy – just the job, as they say. And such is human forgetfulness that, within a week, I felt sure that I could not have held out even for a day without them. What, for instance, could I have used instead of the tin to fetch water from the spring that trickled from under the tamarisk bush on the cliff? And how, without the hammer, could I have flattened the lead for my plummet?

But next to the tin, the most precious find was certainly the spade.

Working at leisure, I spent three days digging a narrow pass through the steepest cliff and cutting steps in it – a sort of earthen stairway to the sea.

I enjoyed this 'earthy', trench-digging work. Where the spade cut it, the clay shone like polished amber. And in the cuts I discovered the unbelievably tough, long roots of some plant which showed an inch and a half above ground.

Everything was wonderful. But best of all was my staggering discovery that very first morning, that this whole dry coast with its thorns, dunes, golden gorse, its winds and sandy beaches and piles of seaweed, its sky and its clouds – the whole of that hot, lilac-coloured shore belonged to no one, or rather, it belonged to me alone.

I met no one for a week.

If I felt like it I could dig a remarkable cave in the cliffs. Or dam the spring and make a pool. Or stack driftwood, fishing floats and old boat frames grey with salt, into pyramids on the beach. Or cut branches of thuya, spread them on the floor and enjoy the smell of resin. There was no one to stop me.

This I ended by doing. My dwelling developed chance but interesting accretions. In the deserted houses round it I found an iron lantern, an hour glass and a Chinese sunshade. All these things I took to my room.

Time Slows Down

The days passed slowly. The sun was in no hurry.

Time slowed down, holding its breath, as though wishing it could stop.

But I knew that the dawn would bring a new day like the one before – so exactly like it that all the days of that week appeared to me as a single never-ending day.

I got used to the hot continuity of that endless day (the nights seemed only to be a break from the merciless daylight), to its monotonous droning, as of a copper string vibrating deep in the earth, to the molten air losing its transparency and clouding like frosted glass, and to the uneven blue of the sky as it deepened or paled under the pressure of the wind.

They say it's good for one sometimes to live alone.

From my own experience of life, I knew that there are many forms of solitude. I won't enumerate them all, but I know there is the solitude you can feel in a crowd, or in a forest, and the solitude that goes with grief, and there is also solitude at sea, which often borders upon a state of silent spiritual exaltation.

This silent state is positively hostile to talk. You want to be silent. And anyway, what can you say in your commonplace words when your dark body, overheated by the day, is suddenly lassoed and refreshed by the most gentle foam whipped up by the evening surf and wind? It melts on you, tingling on your skin with bubbles of sweet-smelling air, its touch as soft and cool as a breeze from those islands where, to this day, perhaps, virgin goddesses of bronze lie sleeping in the earth.

Or its touch may remind you of a girl's hair, damp after bathing.

In that solitude at sea, that face to face encounter with its murmuring expanse, there is always present a sense, if not of immortality, at any rate of the longevity which is the gift of the sea to man.

I spent all day on the beach, until sunset. Often I fell asleep in the shadow of a great rock. I read books a line at a time and I spent hours on end watching the scrolls of the flying clouds. It seems that one of the components of happiness is a state of unconcern, of freedom from even the most trifling of cares.

This must be true, for I was happy then. Pure, primordial, un-adulterated light descended upon earth, and I quite forgot that such immense and gratuitous peace of mind is – according to superstition – never enjoyed with impunity.

Needless to say, retribution came.

I lay on the beach, looking through half shut eyes at spheres of many-coloured flame – they revolved before me in a sort of lilac void. I was trying to work out whether that void was merely the air over the sea, or if the sky had shed its violet blackness, to glitter for a while in silver and pale gold.

While I was reflecting upon this, from the top of the tall cliff came the faint sound of a human cry. I turned, and on the edge of the serene blue sky saw a man waving his cap. He held a small creature by the hand. The creature wore a faded red smock and hesitantly waved an arm as thin as a straw.

'Hullo!' shouted the man. 'Glad to see you in good health, Konstantin Grigoryevich! Come up here a moment.'

My heart sank. Hadn't I known all along that someone would get at me in my retreat and shatter to dust that rarest dream in which I had been living all these days? Even the friendly 'Hullo' rang false and vulgar amidst the harsh heat of the Sarmatian plain, the rustling of its grasses and the sound of the waters of the Pontus.

Reluctantly I rose and started up the cliff, while I tried to guess who the man was and what he could want of me.

'Good for you!' he was shouting. 'Hermit! Recluse! Alex-ander Selkirk! Simon Stylites! Jean-Jacques Rousseau!'

I climbed on, seething, silent for fear of letting out a string of curses at the man who stood on the verge of the rusty earth and the wonderful intensity of the sky and made fun of me.

'Odysseus! Miklukho Maklaï! Sea Wolf! Iphigenia in Tauris! Great Mute!'

I looked up at last, to have it out with the clown, and recognised Vasya Reginin. He was holding his six-year-old daughter, Kira, by the hand and laughing.

'Admit it was a good joke – playing the fool on the shores of that sea celebrated by Academician Aïvazovsky![29] You were furious of course! It's a miracle I've found you. Torelli said you were somewhere here, near Kovalevsky's tower.'

The little girl was holding on to her father's arm and frowning up at me, her eyes an intense dark blue.

'Come to my villa,' I suggested. 'Well, how are things in town? Has anything happened?'

'Nothing much,' he replied, and all of a sudden there were tears in his eyes. They filled, then a few drops ran down his cheeks and fell on his crumpled, washed-out shirt.

'Daddy! You mustn't!' the child said sternly. 'It's all right, I'll stay here, I'm not frightened.'

Wiping his eyes with a handkerchief full of holes, Reginin told me that his wife was ill with typhus, in bed, delirious, and he, being at his wits' end and in complete desperation, had brought me the child because there was nowhere he could leave her in town. He couldn't keep her in the same small room as her mother, he had no friends in Odessa, and so. . . . The child's mouth drooped and her lips trembled.

'It's all right,' she said again. 'I'll stay here with Uncle. . . .'

'Uncle Kostya,' he prompted her. 'Stay, my darling. As soon as Mummy's better, I'll come for you. You will be staying on here for quite some time, won't you?' he asked me.

I was taken aback.

'Yes,' I said. 'Of course. I'll stay as long as necessary.'

'Well then, stay, my kind little heart.' He bent down and kissed the child's head. 'Be good and do what Uncle Kostya tells you. He's our great friend.'

He shook my hand and muttered without looking at me:

'I'll be off then. She's all by herself. She's delirious.'

He turned and went, and I stood bewildered, alone with the little girl on the great hot empty plain. I didn't even notice that Reginin had brought nothing for the child. Not even the smallest bundle of clothes. All she had was what she stood in. I was watching him walk away when I felt her small hot sweaty hand take me by the finger.

Years of Hope

'Let's live like in a game,' she said.

Whatever she meant by it, life in the steppe did indeed from that moment become like a game – something between waking and dreaming.

From that day, fear for the life of that creature, fragile as a dragonfly, held me by the throat and by the heart and never let go of me until at last Reginin sent Torelli to fetch her – but that, as I remember, was not for a full three weeks.

I lived in a state of fear, despair, compassion and tenderness. All these feelings merged into one for which there is no name. At times it weakened, at others even such a trifling thing as pulling a thorn out of a thin, trembling finger flooded me with pain.

But the fact was that I had this small, trusting life on my hands and I had to pull myself together – especially as I had very little food left, no soap and, except for my bedraggled leather jacket, nothing with which to cover the child. And the nights were already getting colder, and more and more often there was a smell of autumn in the room at dawn.

I still don't know how I survived those days without turning grey. I was afraid of everything – the sun (I was always imagining she had sunstroke or heatstroke), the cliffs (how easily she could slip and fall to her death, and how I blessed the steps I had cut in the hard clay), the cold nights (she was sure to catch a chill), storms, and winds, and hunger (I reckoned we had food for only seven days).

All my books and hours of contemplation and happy thoughts were as though they had never been. I suppose because of my terror I failed in those first few days even to notice that the child was forever helping me – sweeping the house and the garden with the wormwood besom, gathering sticks and dry weeds for firewood and fetching water from the spring. True, she was so careful not to spill a drop that it took her an hour to bring it home.

She seldom asked me anything, she preferred to work things out for herself.

She almost never cried. Yet one day when a stone broke off the cliff and fell, cutting her foot, she sobbed as desperately as a child abandoned on a heath at night. She hung on to my neck and trembled all over, while I washed the blood off and tied her foot with a clean rag.

I knew, of course, that she was not crying because of her wounded foot but because of the intolerable grief accumulated in her life over the past days.

The most terrible part of it was not to be able to bury her hot, tear-wet face in her mother's breast and, sobbing and whimpering, realise that in all the world there was only one person who could give her the whole of her tenderness and love and protection, and that person her mother.

Her mother lay sick in Odessa. Her mother might even be dead. But she mustn't think of that or she herself would die. Both of them – she and her mother – were now regretting every hour they had ever spent apart. It was an hour less in which to love each other and an hour nearer to the black incomprehensible void that people called death.

I was convinced that this was exactly how she felt, and I could think of nothing I could do to make her laugh, however seldom. Occasionally she smiled, but I knew it was only to reassure me.

We had to live of course. We lived hard but I was too busy to notice.

I had so many cares, I couldn't even count them.

To start with, washing. We bathed in the sea. But after coming out of that great wash-bowl, our faces spattered with stinging salt, we had to use the fresh but icy water from the spring.

We had no soap; we rubbed our hands and faces with sand. But after a few days I noticed that a strip of limestone at the bottom of the cliff was marbled with bluish petrified silt.

I had childhood recollections of 'keel' soap. It lathered beautifully in sea-water and it was made of some kind of blue Crimean clay. I can even remember the label of the Kharchenko soap-factory in Sebastopol, with its drawing of an anchor and of a bushy-whiskered gentleman, the manufacturer who had bestowed upon mankind the blessings of keel soap.

I scraped off a few lumps of the blue clay and tried rubbing it on my wet hands. It covered them with slime and when I washed it off the skin underneath was perfectly clean.

'It's keel!' I called to Kira.

'Keel, keel, keel!' she called back, shouting for the first time and hopping on her good leg.

Kira collected keel, soaked it, kneaded it like dough, cut it up into small cakes and put them to dry on the beach. Then at last, with infinite care, I washed my shirt and Kira's only dress, and we dried them on the sand.

True, the red dress developed patches of pure grey, and a few holes, but to make up for this it smelt of the sea for a long time.

I was so emboldened by the experiment that I took a few bars of keel and walked with Kira to Sixteenth Station, in the hope of bartering our home-made soap for food.

The first person to whom I offered it – a young fisherwoman grandly named Clarissa – giggled, stared at me with deep reproach, and said:

'Who d'you take me for? Are you pulling my leg? That's just ordinary keel. It's as common as sea water. But I will say your little daughter is as pretty as a peach.'

I explained who Kira was.

'Wait here,' Clarissa ordered. She wiped the sweat off her face with her short, torn skirt, went off to the kitchen garden and came back with a sack full of tomatoes, egg-plants, carrots, peppers and two bunches of grapes.

'All right, just to oblige you, I'll have your keel. And you take this lot and keep the sack.'

I began to thank her.

'What's all that about?' she asked, surprised. 'You crazy? I'm just off to see my Dad, he's fishing off Sanzheyka Cape, but I'll be back in a fortnight. Come and see me. Let's be friends. Don't forget. I know where you're staying – next to Kovalevsky's tower.'

She held out her small rough hand and I had an urge to keep it in mine. Laughing, she pulled it away.

'Don't you try anything on. Or I might take you at your word. Off you go, and look back only once. Just to be polite.'

I went off. I looked back once, saw her laughing eyes and teeth, and decided not to come back.

Somehow, after only a few days, things began to settle down. I found I could read again and, as we sat on the beach, I began to tell Kira stories.

You could not have called them fairytales. No indeed, they were true stories suggested by some incident or other and in no way divorced from reality. I'll give an example.

Playing on the sand, Kira was always finding bits of bottle-glass rolled smooth by the sea. She mistook them for precious stones. She could not believe that they were nothing but plain glass, the kind that littered every waste lot on the outskirts of Odessa.

She was partly right. If glass were as scarce as diamonds, it would be worth its weight in gold.

One day she asked me, 'Where do people dig for glass?' and I had to explain that they didn't dig for it but made it from sand. I began telling her all about it and after half an hour realised to my horror that I was telling it all wrong.

I told her how the one and only seed of a very rare black tulip was sealed inside a glass ball and shipped to Holland, and how that tiny seed caused a war among the flower-growers, and how the war ended only because a boy of two wandered away unnoticed by his nanny who was gossiping, and picked the flower grown from the seed, while the sentry, set to watch it, was hiding behind his striped sentry box, trying to light his pipe in the wind. I told her that many years later Dutch women put up a statue to that boy for saving them from a fratricidal war, for as soon as the unique flower was destroyed there was no longer any reason to fight, and the statue shows the boy tearing the regal black tulip to pieces in a strange childish frenzy.

I never noticed the point at which my story had turned into fiction, and was only brought back to earth by Kira's first and highly practical comment:

'Tulips grow from bulbs, not seeds. We had one at home. And

if you picked it, it came up again the year after. But those naughty Dutchmen didn't know that. They had their silly war all for nothing.'

She thought it over, gave a sigh, and added:

'Fancy flower-growers not knowing!'

I blushed. Not even as a child had I ever been so blatantly caught out in a piece of make-believe. Kira was watching me with narrowed, laughing eyes.

Of course the flower-growers could not have started their war over a tulip seed. At best, they must have started it over a bulb.

Ever since, I have kept firmly to the unwritten law of fairytales and fiction – that every fairystory, even the most unlikely, must have some basis in fact.

Every two or three days we walked to Dry Estuary, about three miles away. There I sat Kira down in the meagre shadow of the dry acacia bushes on the bank, while I waded out to some flat stones and fished for bullheads. This had nothing to do with fishing as recreation. Bullheads were our only fish food.

They swam in shoals in the waters of the estuary. I set myself a minimum of forty to catch each time.

While I fished, Kira sat uncomplainingly in the shade and tried to count the bullheads I caught. She could count only up to ten so for every ten bullheads she put down one empty cockle shell on the ground beside her. When there were four cockleshells she gave me a shout. If I caught any more after that, I counted them myself.

Kira liked her occupation. But her other reason for sitting still and uncomplaining was that the slightest movement would have brought her out of her wretched little patch of shadow into the blazing August sun.

After a while it occurred to us that it would be much less trouble and more pleasant to fish in the late afternoon. Best of all we enjoyed walking home over the endless beaches at sunset, following the very edge of the surf where the sand hardened for a moment after every wave. It was good to walk into the boundless evening haze, while high above it glowed the pink and gold petal of a single cloud.

I had very little flour left. I baked some unleavened flat cakes and then I had none. Icy terror gripped my heart.

I went to Sixteenth Station to see Clarissa but she was still away, staying with her father, and when I asked her neighbour, an elderly fisherman, if he had any flour to sell, he only laughed.

I was turning to go when he stopped me.

'Just a minute.' He took me by the shirt sleeve and fingered the stuff. 'What's this shirt you're wearing? Isn't it English?'

As it happened, it was. I had bartered some rationed tea in the market for an English army khaki shirt.

'What about it?' I asked.

'I'll tell you what,' he said mysteriously. 'Go into the steppe and take the road to Klein-Liebenthal. When you come to a wild pear tree by the roadside, you'll see a gully to your right. Go down into the gully and you'll find a little path. Follow that path and it will take you to a little steam mill – the whole place is no bigger than my hut. There the miller will give you five pounds of flour for that shirt you've got on.'

'It sounds an awful lot,' I said doubtfully.

'He's a very unusual miller,' the fisherman said with the same air of mystery. 'Go along. You'll see for yourself. You haven't heard what's new in politics, by the way? We live like moles here, lucky if we see a paper once a month.'

We set out for the mill that very day.

I should not of course have taken Kira, but I was afraid of leaving her alone.

Dust eddied on the road. We had to keep to the road or we would miss the pear tree and the gully. The incandescent powdered clay burnt our feet even through the soles of our shoes.

Kira walked slowly and began to limp. I picked her up. Panting, she wound her arms, as brown as a gipsy's, round my neck.

I looked round in misery. There was not a patch of shade between me and the horizon, unless you count the brief strokes of telegraph poles with broken wires. Several times we took a short rest in their shadow. All around us, the drought-stricken plain blazed white.

Never once did Kira complain. She kept quiet, resting her chin on my shoulder and gazing wearily at the steppe. Out there, two grey oxen advanced, bent under the yoke. Their tongues lolled almost to the ground. They panted heavily and often stopped. The driver shouted at them in a voice of tearful despair and struck their flanks with a crooked stick. The stick left marks on their sweating hide, like Assyrian cuneiform characters.

Under the pear tree we rested for a long time. Its leaves rustled in the wind like hard wings of beetles.

At long last, at the end of the dry limestone gully, we reached the mill, walked into the yard surrounded by high walls, collapsed in their shadow, and there sat in a kind of daze for an hour, or it may have been two.

The yard was empty. A tin chimney smoked on the tiled roof and from somewhere came the soft hissing of steam.

Then the 'unusual' miller came out, an old man, flour all over him, with an old-fashioned little beard *à la* Chekhov and a pince-nez. The lenses were thick with white finger-marks.

He stopped in front of us, gave us a long look and, without a word, went off to fetch a jug of cold water. We drank, closing our eyes, feeling the freshness flow into us, right down to our finger-tips.

He watched us, silent and impassive, waiting for us to finish.

'Are you the miller?' I asked.

'No, I'm the vine-grower!'

'Why don't you ask what we've come for?' I thought the man must be a lunatic.

A slow, crafty smile lit up his eyes. 'Because I know what you want.'

'Then, can you do it?' I pointed to my shirt. 'That's all I've got.'

'And what will you wear to go back? The heat is fifty degrees in the sun.'

'I'll sit here until it's cooler. I've got another shirt at home, an old one.'

'Then why aren't you wearing it?'

'I don't know,' I answered listlessly. 'I'm tired. I've had no bread for four days.'

'And the girl?'

'She still had some rusks until last night.'

'Wait here.' He went off again, and stayed away a long time.

It was the hottest hour of the day – I could tell from the dull droning in the steppe, like the buzzing of millions of beetles caught in honey.

Instead of the old man an old woman, also covered in flour, came out and brought us six tomatoes, a pinch of salt in a rag, and two chunks of newly baked bread. We ate it all up in a few minutes, down to the last crumb, and immediately fell asleep.

I awoke when shadows, as long as wasted arms, lay on the grey earth. The sun was going out in the dust. A faint coolness drifted from the gully; it even seemed to smell of water.

The old woman stood beside me.

'Get up,' she said. 'And wake up the girl. It's bad for you to sleep at sunset. You'll catch a fever.' She put down a heavy sack of flour on the ground beside me. 'That's for you from Kazimir Petrovich.'

'Thank you!'

I jumped up, undid my shirt and started pulling it over my head.

'Don't,' said the woman. 'It won't ruin us. You'll pay us back later. The idea of it, bless your heart!'

I surprised myself by hugging her and kissing her hand. I wanted to thank the old man as well, but she said he was out. Where could he have gone on this empty plain as flat as a giant dish?

Kira kept quiet for a long time, still only half awake. We crossed a farm cart on the road, loaded with two sacks of corn for the mill. Evidently because of the heat the mill worked at night.

Then Kira felt the soft, cooling dust of the road under her scorched heels and laughed.

'Sparrows have their bath in the dust,' she said. 'I've seen them. I wish I could, too, but I don't suppose you'd let me.'

She was teasing me, her eyes crinkled with laughter.

Slowly one hot day succeeded another but neither Reginin nor Torelli came for us. I was getting seriously worried about Kira's mother. Kira too began to fret and begged me to take her home, while I did everything to avoid the subject and to look calm and cheerful.

Finally I gave in and had even fixed the date of our return when a stupid accident upset our plans.

The fact is that, although I had stolen firewood in Arcadia with Yasha Lifshitz, I am not a thief, I never was and I doubt if I ever will be.

All the same I went to Sixteenth Station to commit another theft – not for firewood this time, but for tomatoes.

I had nothing left to barter for food. I had lied to the miller about having a spare shirt – why, I don't know. The faint hope of Clarissa once more taking pity on the child and giving us a few vegetables, I had to give up. To begin with, she was still away, and besides I realised that in view of such feminine hopes of me as she might harbour, I ought not to put myself in her debt.

I set out on my tomato raid at night and needless to say without telling Kira. The result was farcical. Being short-sighted, I stumbled in the dark, the old watchman known as Budka-Khala-budka yelled, fired, and hit me in the back, below the shoulder blades, with a charge of dirty rock salt.

Appalled by the success of his markmanship, he then presented me with a basket of choice tomatoes. It turned out that I had suffered for nothing.

The salt had fanned out in the wind and not hit me hard. All the same the pain was infernal. For two hours I dabbed the cuts with water from the spring, beating myself over the shoulder with a wet rag. I had nothing to use as a bandage so for two days I sat barebacked in the shade, waiting for the cuts to heal. I told Kira I had scratched myself scrambling down the cliff.

A few days later Torelli and Izya Livshitz came to fetch us.

Torelli came for Kira. Her mother had recovered and was only crying with hunger and sulking because her dark thick hair had been shaved off. Izya came to tell me it was time for me to go back to *The Seaman*.

I returned to Odessa as regretfully as I used to go back to school after a short summer of freedom. I was homesick for the Sixteenth Station, for my beach, and if I hadn't been ashamed, I would have had a good cry in private.

That was the end of this brief episode. Though perhaps it really ended later, at the book fair at the writers' club in Moscow in 1947.

Reginin came up to me with a tall, calm, reserved young woman and said:

'Here you are! That's Kira, the one on whose account you got shot with salt in the backside.'

Kira blushed and held out her hand.

'Do you remember how we lived at Fountain?' I asked her.

'Yes,' she replied uncertainly. 'Well, to be honest, only just. And I'd quite forgotten your face.'

Feeling, for some reason, a little put out I asked, for something to say:

'What are you doing now?'

'I've taken my degree, I'm doing post-graduate research. I'm married. I'd like you to meet my husband. Will you wait a moment?'

She moved away. I waited a few minutes but there was no sign of her. Then I left the club, and could never afterwards explain to myself why I had taken care to slip out unnoticed.

20

Goodbye My Odessa

It was my second autumn in Odessa.

Of all the autumn seasons I remembered, autumn in Odessa seemed to me the most luminous. This was true not only of the steppe, the dachas, the Fountains with their deserted gardens, but of the city itself.

I came across an exact description of autumn in Odessa in a poem I read somewhere:

The autumn air is fine and full of danger,
There is a different rhythm, a different round of days,
The cherished city is more beautiful in autumn,
Its sound more gentle. . . .

In the morning, when the streets were still in shadow, they smelt of dying stocks. Yet I could never find stocks growing in the squares or gardens. Apparently what I smelt were simply the morning shadows, or the freshly watered roadways, or perhaps the faint breeze from the open sea. It blew from the side of Big Fountain lighthouse, over the melon fields where it gathered the sweetish smell of withering stalks and leaves, filtered with difficulty through the dense growth of trees and bushes along French Boulevard and meandered on through the sea-side suburbs, where tomatoes ripened and melon-rinds dried on the roofs of the fishermen's huts.

All this gave the wind its flower-like, clean, refreshing smell. The air was truly 'fine and full of danger' – not only because you could catch a cold but because, having breathed it, you could not stop wishing that autumn would go on for ever in Odessa with its soft conversation and laughter in the streets.

In southern towns, people are less shy of the street than they are in the north, and because of this the streets are more exuberant and lyrical, ready at the drop of a hat to become the stage for human kindness, wit and curiosity.

I have said that the autumn in Odessa is luminous.[30] I came across the word as a boy (Tyutchev speaks of 'luminous evenings') but its exact meaning escaped me for a long time.

Only in old age did I discover that it describes the steady, serene effulgence of the sun's rays, particularly in the evening and in autumn.

Autumn in Odessa was luminous in the fullest sense of the word. A quiet, pinkish light filled the streets. It was pinkish partly because of the perpetual haze, and partly because the sun hung lower and lower above the horizon, and from early morning took on the reddish tints of sunset.

But that year, the bright autumn weather soon gave way to fog. The light faded out. This melancholy change coincided with the unexpected closing down of *The Seaman*.

Allegedly the Sailors' Union could not afford to publish it. But the money could have been found – the paper was exceptionally popular. The real trouble was that the official editor, Pokhodkin, a retired naval captain – grey-moustached, humming with indecision, terrified of all journalists and of his own paper - was always looking for some way of getting rid of it, and eager for any excuse to close it down.

On the day it closed, he could think of nothing better than to hold a wake for it at his villa in Arcadia.

We came to the party in a state of nervous irritation and subconsciously determined to have a row. All we needed was a grievance, however trifling. Naturally, we found one, and it was not so frivolous as all that.

As soon as we came in, we were further exasperated by the faint but disgusting stench of kerosine in all the rooms.

It turned out that the Captain's hobby was rearing chickens.

He proudly showed us the row of incubators on the verandah, a smelly oil-lamp crackling under each one.

In love with sailing, ports, and the magic of the high seas, we took the Captain's chickens and incubators as an insult to our dreams and to the whole seafaring profession.

Instead of proposing the first toast, Bagritsky declaimed a furious tirade against sham sailors, philistines who turned their back to the ocean, on the song of the wind in the shrouds, sweet as the murmur of space in a sea-shell, over the whole of that glorious, unpredictable way of life, and escaped into the stale and stuffy world of incubators.

Next, Ivanov jumped up, overturning his chair, and shouted, spluttering with rage:

'Comrades! That shark in naval uniform,' (his shaking finger pointed at Pokhodkin) 'that wind bag, that old sack of straw, has shut down our wonderful paper! Why? So that he can hatch his rickety chickens to sell in the market! This is more than a disgrace. It's an infamy! It calls for retribution! Break the incubators! Smash them to smithereens, to dust, to smoke! I alone will answer for everything!'

The amount we had drunk was not enough to explain the fact that within minutes nearly all the incubators were broken and smashed. Clouds of greasy soot poured from the oil-lamps. Pokhodkin, ripping the gold buttons off his tunic together with the cloth, was beating his breast and wailing penitently:

'That's right! I've deserved it! I confess!'

His wife, a stumpy little woman with tight red curls all over her head, grabbed our hands, twisted our fingers in impotent fury and hissed:

'Scoundrels! I'll have you all locked up. You won't get away with it.'

No one knows how it would have ended but for the direct intervention of the sea. The villa stood near the cliffs. The cliffs that evening were being pounded by a storm. From somewhere on the cliffs came the crash and rumble of an explosion; the house shuddered and swayed; all the window-glass flew out, ringing merrily. The Captain raised his arms to heaven and roared: 'Quiet! No panic! A mine has exploded on the cliffs. Serves me right! I've deserved it! That clucking hen,' he stamped at his wretched wife, 'knocked all the stuffing out of me.'

Immediately after the explosion we scattered. We ran, we could not get away fast enough from that hateful house, gaping with all its broken windows and still belching soot and the stench of kerosine.

By the beginning of the winter I was all alone in Black Sea Street.

So long as the bright autumn weather held, the lodge was warm and almost cosy but when the heavy rains began, it sucked up water like a sponge. Dark stains spread along the walls. The rooms smelt of lime and whitewash, and hordes of sickly, slow-moving spiders crept out of nowhere.

I had to move to dry quarters. But where?

It was Lucienna, the former typist from *The Seaman*, who saved me. She had joined an arts and crafts team and was sewing un-bleached linen hats for ladies. The team would take on any work so long as it was paid: making hats, clogs, cigarette lighters, sewing brassieres, painting sign-boards for government institutions and plywood posters for cinemas, as well as manufacturing a mysterious powder which served quite well as a substitute for yeast.

The team had set up its workshop on the ground floor of a former dressmaking establishment, Allschwang & Co. The first floor, where the cutting and fitting rooms had been, stood empty and cold. Lucienna suggested that I should move in as a squatter.

The team had no objection – anyone living in the house would make it less likely that their workshop would be burgled.

I moved to Allschwang's. I locked up the lodge and took the key, to keep until the first warm days of spring.

I set up my *bourzhouika* in the fitting room, adapting the chimney to the ventilator. I slept on a large looking-glass door which had been taken off its hinges; I laid it on cases of wood-shavings. Several times a night my worn old mattress slipped off the mirrored surface and tipped me out on to the stone floor.

I had taken a job with another paper, *The Lathe*. What I mostly remember of it is a dingy office, as dark as a cellar, and a crowd of messenger boys with nothing whatever to do. Kurs, the editor – the kindest of men (though he played the ruthless commissar) – had gathered all these urchins and given them bread-cards.

Totally unemployed, they played snap or noughts and crosses all day long, but at least they didn't starve.

It was a dismal winter. The harbour was frozen. Beyond the lighthouse, the Bulgarian ship, *Varna,* lay icebound. It had brought a cargo of olives; the olives were frozen, too.

We had no ships of our own yet. Two old steamers had been towed from the ships' cemetery to the repair-yards and were being put into shape. One was called *Dimitry,* the other *Pestel.*

The kind of job it was can be judged from the fact that three hundred rivets were needed for the *Dimitry* alone, and in two full months not a single rivet had been found in Odessa. *The Lathe* printed a letter on this subject from one of the dockyard workers; it appeared in bold type under the reproachful heading: 'No, Comrades, this is not the way to achieve happiness!'

I was beginning to feel that my time in Odessa had come to an end; I had got all I could out of it. I had had this sort of intuition several times before, and it had never deceived me – it meant that it was time to move. But there was not the slightest prospect of it so far – I had neither money nor a job elsewhere.

One grey, miserable winter day, Izya Livshitz burst into the office, past the little boys playing their exciting games around the stove. He announced that *The Seaman* had been revived and the first new issue would be out next week.

Apparently, some former members of the sailors' revolutionary underground, together with the Bolsheviks, had managed to have it put on its feet again.

This was just as well. Ivanov missed his paper so much that he had taken to his bed and not uttered a word for two months. Marina worked herself to the bone keeping him and the two children. 'A lunatic,' she said of her husband, but with tears of pride in her big dark eyes. 'You know what he says? "A paper like our *Seaman* cannot die." '

Izya and I hugged each other for joy. Kurs came storming from his office in a rage. All the little boys scattered in terror.

Kurs shouted that he wouldn't let me go – it was sabotage, wrecking tactics, a stab in the back, in fact it was counter-revolution. Izya and I only laughed. In the end, he shrugged his shoulders and resigned himself.

How many times have I not learned by experience that the same good thing never happens twice! One should expect happiness, of course, but not the happiness one has already had. Yet such is human nature that we always wait for a miraculous repetition – a resurrection of our past which, embellished by time, seems to us unique and wonderful.

I returned to *The Seaman,* but it was no longer the same. Something had changed. I couldn't put my finger on what the change was, but somehow the paper was a little dry, and life in the editorial office a little less exciting.

So I was delighted when Ivanov suggested that I should go for *The Seaman* on a tour of all the Black Sea ports between Odessa and Batumi. Seventy rivets having somehow been unearthed, the *Dimitry* was being sent on a cruise along the coast of the Caucasus. It was to be the first run of what, so far, was the only Soviet steamer, to places which had only recently been liberated from the Whites.

The *Dimitry* was to carry mines, foodstuffs for the Crimea, and sailors to reorganise the work in the newly-won, hungry and half-ruined ports.

She would also carry a few passengers, and two hundred speculators who were going to the Crimea to buy salt. No one in those days regarded this as strange.

Odessa's parting gift to me was a show such as perhaps no other city could have put on. This was the funeral of 'Sashka the Musician' whom Kuprin has described in his 'Gambrinus'.[31]

While I was in Odessa, I had taken to reading the newspapers from the first to the last word – you never knew when you would run across some pearl of Odessan literary style.

I still remember a funeral notice as striking by its text as by its lay-out:

The mighty oak

KHAIM WOLF SEREBRYANNY

has fallen

and his orphaned branches bow

in deep anguish

Funeral procession to the 2nd Jewish cemetery starts at —, from—.

What could be more affecting than the thought of the 'mighty oak' Serebryanny – some hefty navvy who had breakfasted off a pound of suet and a bottle of vodka every morning of his life – and those 'orphaned branches', his children?

Thus it happened that one day I read in the *Odessa News* the announcement of the death of a certain Aaron Moyseyevich Goldstein (I think that was his name). No one would have paid any attention to it but for the words in brackets after the surname: ' "Sashka the Musician" from the "Gambrinus" '.

Until then, I had believed that characters in fiction are nearly always fictitious. I could not imagine life and literature merging into one. So the announcement puzzled me.

I re-read 'Gambrinus'. It was as precise as the minutes of a meeting, and yet deeply moving and as picturesque as a summer evening in Odessa's Deribasov Street.

What then gave it that quality which I hesitated whether to call authenticity of art or a noble sensibility? Apparently it was the noble sensibility and humanity of Kuprin himself that endowed his story with the character of great art.

It was almost incredible to me that Sashka – the Sashka I had known since my childhood as the hero of a story – had actually been living next door, in the garret of an old Odessa house.

But I was privileged. I was to see with my own eyes the true ending of 'Gambrinus': the funeral of Sashka the Musician, life itself rounding off Kuprin's story.

Goodbye My Odessa

The whole of working-class Odessa from the docks and the suburbs followed Sashka the Musician to the cemetery.

The black cart with the coffin was drawn by skinny horses who often stopped on the way, breathless and wheezing. Every time, the crowd waited patiently for them to recover; then, without any urging from the red-haired driver, they leaned on the traces and walked on a little further. Dull tears of age stood in the splendid eyes of the martyred beasts.

Lowengard, an old reporter from *The Seaman*, walked next to me. The funeral horses reminded him of an old gypsy romance, 'A pair of bays harnessed at dawn': sometimes, at the Gambrinus, Sashka had accompanied Vera the street-singer, nicknamed Cocaine, who sang it so movingly that many of the clients wept.

The red-haired driver smoked, and spat neatly into the roadway. His torn hat pulled over one eye, his whole seedy appearance spoke of how much life had changed since Sashka's day. 'Call it life when to shoe a single miserable devil of a horse costs you close on a million? A million in the old days would have bought you the whole district of Inner-Mills – apricots and gardens and carriages and horses thrown in!'

A large crowd followed the coffin. Old women waddled along, muffled in warm shawls – women who had known Sashka the Musician in the days when they were flashing young beauties. There were hardly any girls in the procession.

The women walked in a body, ahead of the men. It was etiquette among the poor of Odessa to let the women go in front ('That's Odessa for you – not some wretched, one-horse Vinnitsa!'). After them came Sashka's colleagues, grey with cold.

Near the entrance of the boarded-up Gambrinus, the procession stopped. The musicians took their instruments from under their threadbare coats, and the unexpected melody of a sad, old-fashioned love-song drifted over the silent crowd:

> *Not for me, oh not for me*
> *Will come the spring. . . .*

People in the crowd took off their hats, blew their noses,

coughed and wiped their eyes. Then a hoarse, deliberately hearty voice shouted from the back:

'Let's have Sashka's favourite!'

The musicians glanced at one another, nodded, and struck up a boisterous staccato tune:

> *Goodbye my Odessa,*
> *Sweet Quarantine,*
> *Tomorrow we're off*
> *To far Sakhalin!*[32]

I was watching the crowd. All these people – fishermen, sailors, smugglers, stokers, dockers, navvies, a strong, rumbustuous Odessa breed – had once been regulars of the Gambrinus. What had become of them? 'Life has been hard on us,' elderly sailors humbly admitted. 'Life is not to be cheated, you have to be tough with it – lug it on your hump and stow it in the hold like a hundredweight sack. That's what we've been doing, but we haven't seen much happiness yet, and it doesn't look as if we shall, at our age. Look at old Sashka in his coffin, shrivelled as a monkey! Happiness is for the young. Youth at the helm, they say. Well, may they live in justice and freedom. We'll have done our bit towards it.'

Lowengard took me gently by the arm and said:

'It was I who took Alexander Ivanovich Kuprin to the Gambrinus. There he sat over his vodka, grinning and screwing up his Tartar eyes. And then suddenly, a year later, that story came out! I cried over it, you know. That's a real masterpiece of brotherly love, a pearl among the rubbish of our everyday life.'

It was the first I had heard of Lowengard having known Kuprin, but ever since I have thought that if Kuprin had lived long enough he would certainly have written about Lowengard.

A lonely, broken-down old man, Lowengard had one passion – the port of Odessa. He had often refused better paid jobs, and had always stuck to covering the port.

From morning till sunset, whatever the weather and the season, he slowly made his round of the docks, climbed aboard the ships and questioned the sailors about all the details of their trips. He had perfect mastery of several languages, including modern Greek. With equal and exquisite courtesy he spoke to captains and layabouts, always removing his battered old hat.

The port knew him as 'The Chronicler'. In spite of the absurdity of his old-fashioned figure among the loud-mouthed population of the docks, no one ever laid a hand on him or allowed him to be harmed. In his way, he was their Sashka the Musician.

21

Gale Force Eleven

A cargo of floating mines for Sebastopol in her hold and two hundred speculators on deck, the *Dimitry* sailed.

Only Izya Livshitz came to see me off.

It was a fairly cold, still winter day. In place of yesterday's puddles, crusts of ice as thin as mica crackled on the breakwaters. Snow fluttered, so light that it seemed you could count all the snowflakes.

Seagulls beat the water as they took off, as though to warm their cold, red feet.

Standing by the dockside, the *Dimitry* listed heavily. She was smaller than she had seemed from the distance of the Boulevard. Hissing ominously, steam oozed from her every chink and the whole ship smelt like a bath or a laundry.

The deck was cluttered up with sacks and carpet-bags, and lying or sitting on them were the carpet-baggers – women muffled up to the eyes in shawls and men in boots smelling of tar.

I was put into a cabin for four in which we were eight. Three lay on the floor and one, a Volga boatman, sat on the washstand – it could not be used for washing anyway, as there was no water.

To keep him from tumbling down on top of us at night, we tied him with a towel to a clothes hook in the wall.

But the boatman never grumbled. He felt ill at ease among sailors and preferred to stay in the background. He and I were the only civilians – all the rest were in the Navy. The two youngest and I slept on the floor.

Gale Force Eleven

On our very first night out, my neighbour, a former midshipman, now the Captain of the Sanzheyka floating lighthouse, said to no one in particular:

'In case of trouble, I strongly urge our civilian comrades to stick close to us sailors.'

I let it pass, but the boatman nerved himself to ask:

'Do you think the journey will be dangerous?'

'Judging by all the signs,' the midshipman said with relish, 'the *Dimitry* is heading for a watery grave.'

He was ticked off sharply by the Commissar of the Nikolayevsk Port.

There was no sign of danger so far. We sailed in a light mist. Swaying gently, the panorama of the town, the dome of the Opera House and the Vorontsov Palace, then the Fountains and the familiar Kovalevsky Tower receded into the haze. The waves muttered softly in their everlasting chase.

We found boiling water in the galley and, sitting on the floor, drank tea with saccharine.

Towards nightfall the sound of the waves grew louder, but the smell of steam and smoke and the steady rolling of the ship were reassuring.

I fell sound asleep. How much later it was, I don't know, but when I woke up the lamp over the washstand was on, dim and distant as though a mile away, the boatman was swaying back and forth and clinging to the washbasin, my shoulder was being pounded against the cabin door and everything around was creaking and groaning. You could hear the *Dimitry* sighing heavily as she lurched into the water and with difficulty clambered out.

'Listen to that gale,' a sailor said disapprovingly. 'Only been blowing for an hour and it's reached Force Seven.'

The cabin, cramped and airless, gave sudden jerks, trying to throw us into a heap, and pulling us from side to side as though to wipe the floor with us.

The young midshipman half opened the door and looked out. The carpet-baggers had fled the deck and lay packed in a tight row on the floor of the narrow passage. Alone among them an old

Jew in a long frock coat stood upright, his shaking hands pressed against the walls.

Where that old man from the backwoods was going, no one could tell, but he looked wildly improbable on a creaking sea-going steamer, tossed by a storm at night.

'Why are you standing?' asked the midshipman. 'You'll get seasick. You ought to lie down.'

'Can't you see, sir, there's no room for me,' said the Jew.

The midshipman went out, shook the carpet-baggers awake and cleared a space for him.

'An Old Testament character from the time of the Flood,' he said, coming back.

I lay close to the wall and listened to the seas as they shook the steamer, pounding its thin metal side. I was growing uncomfortable. It was strange to realise that, four millimetres from my flushed face, mountains of icy water were galloping through the gloom as though possessed. And what gloom!

I glanced at the porthole. Impenetrable, as though subterranean, darkness lay beyond it, over the primaeval chaos of the unimaginably vast watery waste.

No one slept. Everyone listened. The *Dimitry* gave sharp cracks. It was hard to understand why the mouldering walls, floors and ceilings of the cabins hadn't flown to splinters under the strain of the tossing ship, which bent and loosened every screw, tie, rivet and bolt.

At each crack I looked at the sailors. They were calm, but they were chain-smoking. So was I, while trying to convince myself that there was more life left in the *Dimitry* than I, as an ignorant civilian comrade, could have supposed.

We were all waiting for the morning. But morning was frighteningly far off, beyond the thick darkness howling over half the world.

The tossing grew worse. The ship lay almost flat, now on one side, now on the other. More and more often the screw leapt clear of the water, and each time the *Dimitry* shook furiously and hummed with the strain.

Gale Force Eleven

'Couldn't a storm like that drive us ashore?' the Volga boatman, still clinging to his washstand, asked abruptly.

The sailors were contemptuously silent. Not until about ten minutes later did the grim but kindly Commissar reply:

'The wind has reached Force Ten. Of course, anything is possible. But I wouldn't pin my hopes to being blown ashore, if I were you. The further off we are from it, the better.'

'Why's that?' asked the boatman.

'Because near the coast the ship would certainly break her back on the waves. Or against the rocks. And there would be no survivors.'

And I who had been looking at my watch every ten minutes, waiting for the dawn and hoping that we might be driven to the North Crimean shore and find safety on its stony, barren soil!

In the middle of the night the midshipman got up and, putting on his boots and hooded leather jacket, said casually:

'I'll go and have a look.'

He came back soon, wet from hood to heels.

Tensely silent, we waited for him to speak.

'Speech is silver, silence is gold,' he said mockingly. 'Well, here it is. The deck is awash. Two of the four lifeboats have broken away. The gunwhale's bent. The gale is Force Eleven. But all this is nothing.'

'Nothing, is it?' the Commissar muttered, sitting down on his bunk. 'Well, go on. What else?'

'The forepeak is damaged, and we've sprung a leak.'

'Are the donkey engines working?' the Commissar asked quietly.

'Yes, they're managing so far. But the engine's packing up.'

'Are we moving?'

'That's the point, Comrade Commissar. We aren't pulling.'

'Drifting, are we?'

'Exactly, sir.'

'Drifting towards the Rumanian coast?'

'Yes, sir.'

'But that's where . . .' The Commissar grabbed at the upper

bunk and pulled himself up. 'I'll have a talk with the Captain.'
He went away. We were silent for a long time.

'The joke is,' said one of the sailors, 'that during the war the Germans laid a lot of mines along that coast – scattered handsome bouquets of them, as you might say. And there they still are. If we're driven on to them. . . .'

He didn't have to tell us. We knew what would happen.

The Commissar came back and, still in his leather coat, sat down and lit a cigarette.

The waves boomed and hissed, the whistling of the wind in the rigging grew shriller and shriller. The sound of it chilled your blood.

'We've sent an SOS.' The Commissar paused. 'But it won't do us any good. There are no ships in our ports. And no one will come from the Bosphorous in this storm, not even the *Superb*. So there we are.'

We sat in grim silence. From the corridor came the sound of water splashing from the deck over the raised thresholds.

So a day went by and, amidst the howling of the gale, night fell for the second time. The storm continued; it seemed as though it would not abate until the end of time.

On the third day we all fell into a kind of stupor. Everyone, even old sailors, looked exhausted.

On the fourth day I was sitting, eyes closed and hands pressed to the floor, counting the upward and downward swings of the ship. At moments they seemed less sharp and I hastily lit a cigarette. But the illusory lull was brief, and again my heart lurched as the cabin flew up and sank, leaning sideways, into an invisible void.

At last, terribly slowly, intermittently, as though hesitating, a sullen livid morning dawned beyond the porthole. The whistle in the rigging rose to a demented shriek.

The wind was a northeaster – 'the scourge of God', the sailors called it. From them I learnt that a northeaster blows for three, seven or eleven days.

The carpet-baggers in the corridor stirred and muttered hoarsely; tired women burst into tears. One old woman just outside the door kept repeating the same prayer over and over again: 'Holy God, Holy and Strong, Holy and Immortal, have mercy upon us.' When the tossing became particularly violent she cut the prayer short and only whispered hurriedly: 'Have mercy, have mercy.'

For the first time, I decided to go on deck. According to the sailors, one felt much worse in the cabin than outside.

The Commissar came with me:

'You can't go alone. They won't let you on deck by yourself. Besides, you might be washed overboard.'

Water up to our ankles, in the nauseating smell of vomit, past the carpet-baggers lying prone on the wet floor and groaning, we reached the companionway which led to the upper deckhouse and the deck.

The Commissar leaned hard on the deck-house door. It flew open and a rush of air flung us outside.

Clutching at an ice-slick rope, I saw what in the dark cabin I had only imagined – a titanic, an unheard of storm. It filled me with an overwhelming sense of despair and of terrifying beauty.

A pitiful human dustmote rapidly losing the last of its warmth, I stood facing it – while the storm thundered and drove iron waves before it, hurled them into dark abysses, erupted at the swollen sky, rolled mountains of water and, rending the air, plastered us with sticky foam.

The *Dimitry*'s stern flew up to the clouds and sank deep into the water. Long, steep waves reared and swept the sea from side to side of the horizon; their crests ran before them, and in the furrows was revealed, in all its terrifying majesty, the churning of the leaden waters of that hurricane region we would have to cross in order to survive.

'Look!' the Commissar shouted.

I couldn't understand what he was pointing at.

'Look at all that vapour!'

Then I saw – between the howling waves, swift, angry jets of steam shooting from the grey-green water like the gunsmoke from a thousand guns.

Later, in the cabin, the Commissar told me that such jets appear whenever a warm sea is invaded by an ice-cold storm.

Then I saw the horizon in front of us blotted out and a gigantic wall of raging sea bearing down on us with a cosmic boom. The Commissar seized my arm and pulled me inside the deckhouse. 'Hold on!' he shouted.

Darkness filled the deckhouse. With a rending noise, the *Dimitry* rushed up the watery slope, then paused and, shuddering, sank into water up to the Captain's bridge. 'It's all over,' I said to myself. 'If only I can stop myself from screaming with terror!'

With a muffled groan, the ship rolled over on its side, and beyond the porthole, wide sheets of water cascaded from the deck, back into the sea.

'What was that?' I asked stupidly.

'Another two or three such seas and it's all up with us,' said the Commissar, looking at me with glazed, wide-open eyes.

But there were no more waves like that one. The sea still roared dementedly, but the *Dimitry* seemed to pitch a little less.

We recovered our breath and went back to the cabin. The wind was no longer shrieking but humming steadily in the rigging and the ship's funnel. There was a sudden lull in the violence of the gale.

The boatswain, his face scalded by the northeaster, looked into the cabin and said that the engine was pulling once again, and we were making headway, though slowly, against the storm.

The sailors cheered up. They even rummaged in their boxes and bags and got out their meagre rations.

I was blissfully chewing a piece of barley-bread when, through the noise of the sea and wind, there came the choking, spluttering wail of the ship's siren.

The sailors blenched and jumped up. For hundreds of miles around us there was nothing but the turbulence of the stormy sea. What could the siren mean?

Hastily buttoning up their greatcoats, they rushed up on deck. I followed. I prepared myself to see the end of the *Dimitry* and all that horror of slow disaster contained in the word 'shipwreck'.

But nothing terrible had happened. The sea still drove its mountainous waves. Some sailors were running along the quarterdeck, pulling on a rope.

'What was the siren for?' the Commissar shouted to them.

'We've sighted land! Cape Tarkhankut!' one of them called back.

The Commissar swore in astonishment and went up to see the Captain. I scrambled up the narrow, slippery companionway after him.

I had met the Captain in Odessa. He was an exceptionally thin and exceptionally serene old man with snow-white hair.

'Sorry about that,' he said. 'The mate was on watch with me, he sighted land and got so excited that he sounded the siren. Startled everybody. Still, it's excusable, I suppose. He'd never been in a storm like that before.'

'And you,' I asked, 'have you often been in such a storm?'

'Where? On the Black Sea?' He pulled back a corner of his hood to hear better.

'Yes.'

'About twenty times, perhaps,' he answered with a shy smile.

His grey, faded eyes watered in the wind and his hand shook on the gunwhale.

'It was easier before the war,' he said. 'But now the sea is spiked all over with mines. The gales have torn them from their moorings and set them adrift. So you never know when a mine will hit your bottom.'

The Commissar lowered his binoculars and said sheepishly: 'I can't seem to find the coast. Nothing but those blasted waves.'

'No, I don't suppose you can yet. It's still too far,' said the Captain. 'But have a look at the sky. Over there, just above the horizon – can you see a dark strip in the clouds? That's where the land is. It's a kind of reflection it throws up at the overcast.'

The chief engineer came up on the bridge, his angry face as red as a pepper.

'Aristarkh Petrovich, you can't do this,' he pleaded with the Captain. 'Go down to your cabin and rest. The wind is dropping.

The engine is pulling normally for the time being. It's suicide at your age to stand on the bridge for three days and three nights without sleep. The crew want to send a wireless message to complain about you to the management and to your wife.'

'That's as may be,' the Captain grinned. 'The wireless operator won't send anything without my permission. But I'll go and lie down for a bit. In three hours' time we'll be entering Karadzhi Bay.' He pointed at a small circle on the map. 'Here it is. Just north of Tarkhankut. We'll stay there and ride out the storm. Until then I think I'll get some sleep. You'll excuse me, Comrades.' He went to the companionway but turned back and asked the Commissar:

'Are they your men, that crew of six sailors we've got on board?'

'No.' The Commissar pricked up his ears. 'They're from Odessa. Why?'

'They're cut-throats, that's why. They pushed their way on board and refused to show their documents. One of them wears a silver anklet. You might check up on them.'

'I certainly will.'

'A bad lot. Riff-raff,' the chief engineer put in. 'Jailbirds in disguise. Armed from neck to navel. Lucky the storm knocked them out or they'd be raising hell.'

He went down. The Commissar and I spent a few more minutes with the mate who had replaced the Captain on watch.

We looked at the sky, pale-leaden in the east, and at the dark strip of cloud like a motionless trail of smoke. If that was a reflection of the land, we were still very far away from it.

We wished we could stay longer on the bridge, but the rules of naval courtesy forbade it so we went down.

Below, the cabins and gangways rang with excited voices. Everybody knew by now that we had sighted land, and that if we were being tossed less violently it was because that distant, blessed shore had already taken us under its wing and protected us from the icy northeaster.

In the middle of the night there came the long-drawn-out running rumble of the anchor-chain. The sound was repeated twice: the *Dimitry* had cast anchor in Karadzhi Bay near Tark-hankut.

From the earliest times, Cape Tarkhankut has been held in ill repute by seafaring men. The sea around it is never calm, pre-sumably because several crosscurrents meet at this point. The waters seethe around the Cape and the short but choppy crossing upsets passengers and exasperates the crew. In the days of sailing vessels so many ships were wrecked that the place was ominously known as the 'ships' graveyard'.

We stood at anchor. We rolled very gently, and at times even this mild rocking ceased. Then everyone sighed with relief.

I went out on deck. The wind lashed my face with pellets of snow. Iron darkness lay all around. In this gloom, very near but not inside the bay, the surf thundered for hundreds of miles to north and south. Like slow lightning, the lamp of the Tarkhankut lighthouse flashed on, swept the boiling sea with its grey-white beam and went out.

I went back to my cabin. The whole ship was fast asleep. Only the young midshipman looked up and mumbled something that was trying even now to be a joke about 'sleeping like the dead in a dead calm'. But he must at once have dropped his head back on his suitcase and dozed off. I say 'he must' because I didn't see him do it – before the words were out of his mouth I sank into bottomless lethargy.

In the morning we saw that the *Dimitry* lay clanking her chains close to the rust-brown shore. There is perhaps no other place in the whole world as poor and wretched as the bay that had saved our lives.

A few tufts of blackened grass dotted the bare saltmarsh, and caked snow glittered in the hollows.

The plain, level as a taught string, receded into muddy mist. Above the mist scudded low clouds, dropping charges of hard snow. There was not a man or a bird, or a ruined hut or well, there was not even a stone that might at least have looked like a gravestone on the whole of that dark-brown coast.

Yet although it is often said and for the most part justly, that human beings are ungrateful, that morning after the cruel storm, I felt deeply and genuinely grateful for that bay and its wretched soil.

It might have been a Biblical desert, a land that God had cursed from now to all eternity. But its desiccated and barren body shielded us from the merciless elements. Within a stone's throw, the sea battered the shore so furiously that it shook under the impact.

The Commissar of the Nikolayevsk Port lent me his naval binoculars and, from behind a warm housing on deck, I looked at the coast for a long time, hoping to see someone. But neither a human being nor a sign of human habitation was anywhere to be seen.

It was impossible to believe that this really was the Crimea, the Taurida, that within some eighty miles the sun lay warm and fragrant on beechwoods.

We spent four days in Karadzhi Bay. The storm continued unabated, and every time I caught sight of the pewter sea bellowing without rhyme or reason, I felt sick at heart.

In the course of these four days the *Dimitry* assumed the appearance of a guard-ship – one of those communal dwellings for retired deckhands and dockers in which they huddle with their bedraggled and quarrelsome families.

There used to be such guardships in all the large ports. Old, disused, dilapidated steamers were set aside for this purpose, and moored in some out of the way corner of the docks so that they shouldn't spoil the contemporary scene.

In no time at all the guard-ship developed all the characteristics of a landlubber with a highly domesticated life – clothes lines, washing (of all colours but mainly, for some reason, lavender or muddy pink), battered zinc tubs; wire cages in which rabbits with red-currant eyes sat smacking their lips; aged tom-cats washing themselves on the crosstrees with the airs of retired admirals; puppies yapping at the seagulls that picked at the garbage floating around the ship.

Gale Force Eleven

Standing at anchor, the *Dimitry* fluttered with drying clothes. They were washed in seawater, without soap, so they were stained a spotty yellowish grey. All over the ship the air was thick with the smell of domesticity.

During the storm, the carpet-baggers, past caring, had looked on with indifference at their most precious possessions flying overboard. Some had even assisted the crew.

But now that the danger of death was past, they took to grumbling and accusing the Captain of being high-handed. Besides, there was nothing to eat.

Taking advantage of the rule covering 'accidents at sea', the Captain ordered the hold to be opened and our small cargo of barley for the Crimea to be distributed among the passengers. It could not be cooked – the storm had put the galley out of action, and in any case, we were very short of fresh water.

The passengers sifted the barley from the mouse-droppings with which it was liberally mixed, and then crunched it raw, like sunflower-seeds.

Water was used sparingly on the *Dimitry*. We were rationed to half a litre a day of the cloudy remnants, smelling of rust, at the bottom of the tank.

I had read as a schoolboy about the traditional mutinies on sailing ships – smoking pistols, and captains thrown overboard by their mutinous crews – but in no possible circumstances had I imagined myself seeing with my own eyes a mutiny in our time, on our peaceful Black Sea, near the blessed shores of the Crimea.

The revolt was started by the 'riff-raff' – six sailors in enormously wide bell-bottoms – and a section of the speculators who joined them.

'Why are we stuck here all this time?' the riff-raff shouted.

It was explained to them that the storm was still blowing and that, between Tarkhankut and Sebastopol, there were vast minefields which it would be madness to attempt to cross in this weather.

The riff-raff and the speculators sent delegates to the Captain. After hearing them out he said that the ship would stay where she was for as long as necessary, and that it was no business of the passengers to meddle with navigation.

'And if we starve to death – is that our business?' roared the riff-raff. 'There are plenty of captains who'd sail straight through the mines – they aren't yellow. Why should we croak on account of that bastard? Let him put on steam and get a move on or we won't waste time talking to him – we'll chuck him overboard. He's not worrying about us – he's just shaking for his own skin. We'll take the ship over ourselves. There's nothing to it.'

It was our third day in Karadzhi. The boatswain knocked and, coming in, said in a low voice that the riff-raff and the speculators were milling outside the Captain's door, yelling, trying to break in and threatening to throw the old man overboard.

The Commissar got up, put his greatcoat on, picked up his Mauser and told us to stay in the cabin unless we heard a revolver shot. His face, the muscles in it bulging like whipcord, looked savage.

We waited for the shot but it never came. The wildest rumours reached our cabin. The Commissar was said by the crew to have immediately gone over to the riff-raff. He was seen going into the Captain's cabin, and was heard shouting. Coming out, he told the riff-raff that the old man was no better than a wet rag and a counter-revolutionary, but there was no point in chucking him into the sea. They should elect one of themselves to replace him. This, however, was a serious step, they would have to answer for it to the government, so they ought to talk it over quietly on their own, without interference from civilians and mercenary souls like the speculators.

'We'll go into the hold. We'll talk it over and choose our captain. Come on, boys.'

As soon as he and the boys were inside the hold, the crew – acting on the Captain's orders and with lightning speed – battened it down with thick boards, screwed them into place, and for greater safety piled a lot of heavy packing cases on top. They evidently felt it was a tricky job for, although they grinned, their hands were shaking.

Gale Force Eleven

Muffled curses, howls of rage and several shots came from the hold. The riff-raff were firing upwards at the boards – but it was quite useless, they couldn't possibly get out.

We realised at once that the Commissar was in league with the Captain and had deliberately lured the cut-throats into the hold. 'Just like Ivan Susanin!'[33] the midshipman said happily. We were worried that there was no food or water in the hold but glad that the Commissar had managed not to give himself away – it would certainly have been the end of him.

'Keep away from the hold! Stand from under!' the boatswain shouted from time to time, just to be on the safe side.

By nightfall the storm began to die down. The *Dimitry* weighed anchor and, her engine working at half-speed, sailed into the open sea. She started to roll at once but, compared to her tossing in the storm, this seemed to us as gentle as the rocking of a cradle.

In the morning I was awoken by sunlight pouring into the cabin. Even through the grey crust of salt on the porthole, the sky was radiantly blue. The ship was steady and only throbbed quietly to the vibration of the screw.

I rushed out on deck and blinked the tears from my eyes. It was several minutes before I could see clearly.

The *Dimitry* was sailing through deep, dense blue light. It was hard to tell where the blue of the sea became the blue of the sky. Cast in gold, the steep cliffs of Cape Lucullus glittered on our port side.

Melting icicles broke from the rigging and smashed into powdered snow on deck.

Behind the stern lay the inky wall of the receding fog. And in the quiet of the bays, in the sparing radiance of the winter sun, in morning clarity and in all its vivid, colourful seaside charm, Sebastopol stood revealed, as majestic as a Russian Acropolis.

22

Crimean Acropolis

A cutter manned by armed sailors met us at the entrance to North Bay. They boarded the ship, opened the hold and called down:

'Happy landings! Come out one at a time! And look sharp! The ringleader last!'

The 'riff-raff' climbed out on deck. They were searched, disarmed, arrested and removed.

The Commissar was told civilly: 'The Port Commandant is coming for you himself.' But of course nothing of the sort happened, as the Commissar, grinning into his tobacco-stained moustache, had known perfectly well.

The *Dimitry* made fast at the passenger berth in South Bay. The passengers were told that this was the end of the road for her. She had sprung another leak, her plates were parting at the seams, the engine had been very nearly pulled from the seating, so she was being towed straight to the ships' cemetery.

I felt sad for her, especially when the tug sailed up and the *Dimitry,* with a farewell hoot, followed it slowly to the dump.

When all was said and done, that noble and decrepit ship had made a supreme last effort, ploughed through an icy storm and saved us all.

I went ashore. The other passengers had scattered without my noticing it. I was left alone.

Where should I go? First, to the Count's Bay to take a look at Sebastopol wrapped in its ancient yellowish haze, and to decide what to do next. I had no friends in the town, unless you count the girl-poet[34] – and I had forgotten her address and even her name.

I sat on a bench, warming myself in the weak sunshine and dozing in the quiet and the relief of having come through my stormy journey.

I must have sat for a long time, until the mist was touched with crimson, and a cold gust blew from the sea where a bell-buoy lowed mournfully on Constantine Reef.

I decided to go to the Sailors' Union, the only refuge to which I had a right as a member of *The Seaman*'s staff.

After hearing me out, the secretary, an old sailor with sad Ukrainian eyes, sat looking at me in silence for such a long time that I thought he had forgotten me. I gave a tentative cough.

'It's you I'm thinking about,' he said. 'You say you have no bread at all? And no roof over your head? That's bad.'

He thought about it for a few more minutes; then he bent over a pad made of scraps of wrapping paper, and began to write a long screed, checking it carefully as he went along and inserting the punctuation marks. Next to Blagov, he was the worst punctuation fanatic I ever met.

'Here you are,' he said at last. 'Go to Sadovaya Street, to the former residence of Admiral Kolans. Give this note to the Admiral's widow – and don't be scared of her, remember you're a staunch Red sailor. She lives with a few hangers-on in a side wing in the yard. We've turned the main building into a kindergarten of a sort. For children of sailors. There's no kindergarten to speak of – we just heat it occasionally and manage to keep them fed, more or less. Anyway, you can sleep there. But you have to be out between eight and five, when the children are there. And mind you don't freeze to death. That would cause me a lot of trouble.'

He handed me another slip, an order to the naval bakery to issue me with a loaf of bread.

'You'll have to eat it a crumb at a time. As it is, I'm stretching a point for you. How long are you staying in Sebastopol?'

'I'm not sure. We've been put ashore by the *Dimitry*. I'll have to wait for the other steamer from Odessa.'

'The *Pestel*?'

'Yes.'

'And what if she doesn't come?'

'Why shouldn't she?' I asked, startled.

'Because the *Pestel* is an old tub as full of holes as the *Dimitry*. Before she comes she has to get here. That's the problem.'

This was unarguable.

'The *Pestel*,' I said, discouraged, 'was supposed to sail a week after us.'

'Oh, well,' he said uncertainly. 'If you do run out of bread, we might manage a little bit more. We'll see. . . .'

I thanked him and set off for the bakery. There was nowhere I could go before five anyway, and it was only three.

The bakery was in the third yard in a small side street. An armed man stood at the gate. He looked at my order slip and let me through.

The baker fetched a loaf of bread but asked me before handing it over:

'What are you going to wrap it up in? And how will you carry it home? Haven't you got anything to put it into?'

I had neither a newspaper nor a bag.

He gave me a reproachful look. 'They'll take it from you before you're out of the yard. How can I issue you with bread? There's no point in my handing you a loaf.'

'They won't really grab it, will they?'

'Have you dropped from the moon or what?' he asked crossly. 'They'll grab it and they'll tear it to pieces. Night and day they're watching at the gate. Yurka!' he called out.

A boy of about ten came from the back-room; he was so thin, there seemed to be nothing left of him except his eyes.

'Take this queer fish with his bread through the Izhitsa Passage to Midshipman Boulevard,' the baker told him. 'And see that nothing goes wrong. And you, Comrade, hide the loaf under your coat. And don't think of eating it on the way. Not a crumb! If they spot it, it's all up with you. *They*,' he stressed, '*they* watch everyone like hawks.'

'Who are "they"?' I asked.

'Honest to God, Comrade, you must have landed straight from Mars! What d'you mean – "who"? People who are hungry, of course.'

The boy took me through the back of the bakery into a narrow alley between high walls. In one of them there was a small gate. He opened it with a huge brass key and we climbed an outside iron stairway, cluttered up with vases of dead fuschias, to the first floor of an old house.

Using a nail, the boy skilfully picked the lock of an oak door carved with swords and banners, and we entered someone's flat.

'Go in quietly,' said the boy, 'and don't be frightened. But don't talk to anyone. Just say how d'you do, if you want to.'

He pushed the nearest door and we walked into a drawing-room with a grand piano, portraits of important-looking admirals with long side-whiskers, and an aquarium without any water in it but overflowing with black potato peelings and beginning to smell. An old lady, tiny and yellow as a canary, lay on a sofa.

'In and out all day,' she said. 'And they pretend to have manners! They say "How do you do". No one asks you to say "How do you do".'

I hurried sheepishly after Yurka, into what must have been the dining-room.

A handsome, tousled, sleepy young man's head poked out from behind a Chinese screen. He looked at Yurka and shook his fist.

'You watch out!'

'Don't you throw your weight about,' Yurka burst out. 'I've been before and I'll come again. What did you think we were giving you bread for? Your outstanding services to the Revolution? Parasites!'

The head bobbed out of sight.

Next door, the kitchen was hung with cobwebs. A pretty girl without a spot of colour in her face, sat in the middle of the room. She had hitched her skirt over her swollen knees, and was staring at them, rubbing them with her hands, and weeping.

Outside the kitchen we crossed a dried-up garden, climbed over a low wall, and found ourselves at the end of Midshipman Boulevard; it was deserted. Yurka said goodbye to me and turned to go.

'That was the "Izhitsa" Passage,' he explained before leaving me. 'It's the safest way. We use it for women and unarmed men. Well, good luck with your loaf. For God's sake don't start nibbling it on the way.'

I sat till five on a broken-down bench in Midshipman Boulevard. A graveyard silence hung over the town.

Only once did a hand-cart rattle noisily over the cobbles. I caught sight of it through the dry branches of the thuya hedge.

Two young women were pulling the cart. A man, barefoot and naked to the waist, was lying on it face-down. It took me a moment to realise that he was dead.

I started for Sadovaya Street.

The town seemed petrified. Here and there a putrid stench came from the back of the yards. Shrivelled ivy scraped softly on the weather-beaten walls. It was hard to believe that warm sunshine ever touched their mouldering stone.

I was irresistibly reminded of a couple of years earlier. In the features of Sebastopol, destitute and dying, I recognised those of Odessa and Kiev in times of typhus and famine.

A harsh, cutting wind rose, evidently from the north. Immediately, all along the street, warped sheets of iron set up their groaning on the roofs. Snow, quite unlike our Russian snow, blew sideways in the wind. It was grey, and mixed at once with the heaps of dry acacia leaves crumbled to dust on the pavements. Drifting out to sea, the slate-coloured sky seemed to take with it the last of the light and warmth and the last gentle, human voices.

I hurried past gaping, broken windows of basements, afraid to look inside. It was there they evidently dragged the corpses before carting them away.

But Sadovaya Street ran through the upper part of the town, and even in the leaden light of the fading day it seemed to me to have that air of quiet cosiness you often find in a remote, weed-grown, dead-end alley.

Crimean Acropolis

I soon came to the single-storey house of Vice-Admiral Kolans. The wrought-iron gate was decorated with anchors, and there was a flag-pole in the courtyard. For some reason, it had not been chopped up for firewood.

The side wing, at the back of the courtyard, was thickly overgrown with wild vines.

I knocked. From behind the door a woman's low-pitched voice asked me whom I wanted to see. I answered. The door swung open and revealed an old woman as tall as a grenadier, white hair stacked on her head and a bent poker in her hands, standing on the threshold. She was leaning on the poker; her eyes flashed fire.

'I,' she said, 'am the widow of Vice-Admiral Caesar Alexandrovich Kolans. But I don't remember you among my husband's friends, young man. And I never forget a face. So say what you have come for, but be clear and brief.'

Instead of replying, I handed her the note from the secretary of the Sailors' Union. She took it between two fingers, shook it as though to flick off the dust and said, turning:

'Read it, Maria.'

A girl as thin and pale as a ghost, with dark rings under her eyes and a church taper in her hand, advanced from the shadows. Without looking at me once, she read the note and, in her turn, called over her shoulder:

'Andrey! This gentleman is going to stay in the kindergarten. Come and show him the way.'

'Have you got any bread?' the widow asked suddenly.

'Very little.'

'No matter.' She struck the floor a sharp blow with her poker. 'I offer you a fair exchange. A little of your bread for a little goat's milk every day. I keep a goat!' Striking the floor again, she turned to the young man called Andrey who had come in and stood modestly in the dark. 'And why shouldn't I? In these circumstances – remember this, Andrey – the late Empress herself would have kept a goat and milked it with her own hands.' She struck the floor for the third time and raised her voice: 'With her own hands, I tell you. – Do you agree?'

'You mean, about the late Empress. . . ?' I asked.

'Don't be silly. The Empress was a fool and a drug addict. That Hessian fly!³⁵ We wouldn't have had this revolution without her. I am asking you if you agree to the exchange.'

'Yes,' I said hastily.

'A pound of bread, that's all.' With a final blow of the poker she gave her orders to Andrey: 'Take the key and let this man into the main house.'

Turning to me, she added:

'But no nonsense, mind. No smoking, no rolling yourself up in the carpet to keep out the bugs' (Maria clasped her hands and gave a gasp) 'and no drinking eau-de-Cologne or any other filth. So long as God gives me strength I'll cope with anyone, be he the arch-commissar himself. Or Beelzebub or Satan. Goodbye.'

She turned and went off into the darkness at the back of the hall, her poker tapping. Maria raised the candle so that it lit up my face, and dropped it with a cry. The light went out. The girl ran after the widow, shouting:

'O God! Mama! It's him, I do believe it's him! Mama! My God!'

'Let's go,' said Andrey. 'I can't stand hysterical women. Sorry, I haven't introduced myself: former Midshipman Andrey Caesarovich Kolans, now goat-herd to my Mama – previously Mine Officer on the former War Transport Ship formerly called *Ratmir*.'

There was nothing to sit or sleep on in the kindergarten. Toddlers' chairs and tables were the only furniture. I sat on the windowsill or the floor, where I also slept. Contrary to the widow's orders, I wrapped myself for the night in the large, dusty, moth-eaten carpet.

I rolled it into a tube, tied it with telephone flex and crawled in head first. In the morning I crawled out the other end. During the night I covered the distance from one end of the carpet to the other.

This woollen pipe became my sure and even cosy refuge throughout my stay in Sebastopol. Wandering aimlessly through the frozen streets, I waited only for the night, for the moment when I could creep inside my rug and get a little warmth into my bones, and dream the strangely consistent dreams which came to me night after night. I suppose it was the stuffiness that brought them on.

I dreamed about small towns set among rocks and gardens on the banks of rushing rivers or on the seashore where the beech-woods came tumbling to the very edge of the sands.

They were all inhabited by people I knew. There, I often met Lyolya and Old Uncle Nechipor, my father, Vrubel, the Sailor from the *Azimuth*, my Latin teacher Suboch, the poet Voloshin and the orderly Antoshchenko, Gronsky the 'little knight', Professor Gilyarov, Sytin the typesetter, and Ivan Bunin, and Lucienna, and Amalia Knoster.[36] With each of them I felt strong ties and a deep and moving relationship. Often, in my dreams, I searched desperately for a friend, knowing that he too was searching for me and that our meeting would be marked by rare and joyful events, but also that it would never take place.

Thinking about those dreams I realised that my life had been very long, whereas the years had always seemed to me brief and swift, vanishing almost without a trace. I was reminded of Fet's poem:

Life has flown and left no trace.
My soul was in a fever – to go where?

Hardly anything in it was any longer true or relevant for me, yet I delighted in repeating it to myself – perhaps because of the sharp contrast between the poem and the events around me.

There had been many such poems ever since the time of Pushkin and Zhukovsky[37] and they still survived. They lived on amidst hunger and sickness and battles, amidst enthusiasms, executions, anger and self-sacrifice, amidst unbelievable poverty and un-shakable faith in the future, and they confirmed me in the simple truth that the heart of the nation remained whole and that this nation could not be destroyed in either body or spirit. I already realised that the suffering of those years could only enhance the grandeur of the country's heroism in those years of hope.

But all these thoughts and recollections of poetry and of dreams were cut short when the moment came to crawl out of my carpet into icy daylight and the chill of the grey walls. Immediately my head began to ache from the cold.

I went to the Admiral's widow, drank, standing, a cup of warm goat's milk, and went out.

Sometimes I went out with the Midshipman and the goat Martha. Her dirty, greasy coat had the grey sheen of stale candle-wax or of rancid lard.

The Midshipman pulled her on a rope and we walked to Historic Boulevard, where the goat cropped the remnants of dry grass on the site of the heroic bastions of the Siege of Sebastopol.

In the course of these outings the Midshipman told me that his sister Maria was a psychopath and a religious maniac. Every other day she had a Requiem said at the Cathedral for Admiral Kolchak, [38] yet in every undersized man she met she thought she recognised Kolchak in disguise, on the run from the firing squad. She had mistaken me for him as well, as she had shouted to her mother on the evening of my arrival.

I spent long hours talking to Andrey on Historic Boulevard. I had nowhere else to go. We each slowly chewed a small chunk of stale bread. It had a crust of plaster on it, and it seemed to me that everything else in Sebastopol was white with plaster as well. The plaster came off the walls of the houses and crunched under-foot.

In the middle of the day I went to the Sailors' Union and had a plate of soup in the canteen. There I also managed to write, and had several pieces for *The Seaman* transmitted over the port wireless. One was about the *Dimitry* gallantly fighting the storm; another about an incident which would pass unnoticed nowadays but which dumbfounded me at the time.

A school was being built near Admiralty Bay. The whole undertaking seemed to me fantastic.

Covered with snow dust and staggering from weakness, the builders dug the foundations, struck the unyielding soil with their picks; gasping and breathless, they had often to sit down on the yellow boulders of Inkerman stone, to rest and wipe with their sleeves their eyes reddened and watering in the relentless wind from the sea.

Every blow cost them a tremendous effort, yet the foundations went deeper with every day, until at last the first huge blocks of sandstone were laid in the trenches.

At the time, this event, so ordinary in itself, struck me as a miracle – and it was indeed a miracle of courage, by which the great hope of the future seemed to be materialised.

After leaving the canteen I usually walked to South Bay, where the cliffs reverberated to the ceaseless shooting at cormorants, or else to the market where food was offered in exchange for medicines or gold – but no one had either gold or medicine.

One day I started out for Khersones, but I never reached it. So desolate was the slatey, smoke-grey distance of the steppe, so harshly – like small rattles – did the grasses crackle in the wind, so mournfully groaned the sea rolling its funereal foam over the beach, that my heart was weighed down with loneliness and I turned back.

I had been stuck in Sebastopol for almost a fortnight. The Sailors' Union had received a wireless message from Odessa that the *Pestel* was about to sail, but there was still no sign of it. It might have put off sailing, or it might have been lost at sea – no one could tell.

I roamed the town, occasionally dropping in at the famous 'Panorama', where there was never a soul and where the huge painting by Rubo[39] shook in the icy draught.

Always looking for some warm place, I went into the Cathedral. There the cold struck through the thin soles of my boots, but near the altar a few candles were burning, and the associations of warmth with fire warmed me a little. But still I shivered all day long.

At last another message arrived, saying that the *Pestel* had left Batumi and would reach Sebastopol within twenty-four hours. I left the kindergarten and moved to the quayside. There were several of us waiting for the *Pestel*. We were allowed to spend the night in the harbour-station, in a small room papered with sailing schedules yellow with age.

Years of Hope

I was glad of the shelter, if only for a few hours. An iron stove, still warm, stood in the corner of the room.

Its warmth seemed to us so genuine a miracle, such an unheard-of happiness that, sitting near the stove, an old woman wept.

The *Pestel* arrived in the morning. The sea was dead calm. Suddenly in the distance appeared the beautiful outlines of an old-fashioned steamer with a sharp bow and bowsprit. Still wrapped in the mysterious yellowish haze which obscured the horizon, she sailed slowly towards Sebastopol. The city was itself enveloped in a reddish mist gilded by the sun.

It was a beautiful marine day, all freshness and pale-blue light. But still more beautiful, and lovable and undeservedly forsaken, seemed Sebastopol as the imperious whistle of the steamer sounded over its bays numbed by the calm. It seemed to shatter the stagnant silence into a thousand splinters, and the splinters to fly echoing along the misty blue coast and to fall, with a final plaintive tinkle, beside Cape Aya and Laspi, over Foros and Meganom and Karaganda – over all the capes and the sea-rolled beaches of the Crimea, as yet unawakened from its half-death, starving, yet as ever magical.

On the morning of my departure Sebastopol arose before me once again in all the simple majesty of an Acropolis, a city conscious of its beauty and its prowess, one of the finest in our land.

23
Dead of Night

The day the *Pestel* sailed from Sebastopol was warm and damp.

Clear grey water licked the steamer's flaking sides, trying to wash away the stains of petrified salt.

But it was wasted effort. For shabbiness and cramped quarters, the *Pestel* could almost have given points to the *Dimitry*.

I went aft. At each turn of the helm its metal coupling bolts grated with strain, a torrent of rushing foam surged from behind the stern, and the bowsprit, as the sailors said, 'rolled' to one side or the other.

Ashen daylight fell on Sebastopol through the clouds. In this soft light you could guess at the nearness of the sun. At times I even felt as though my face were warmed by its unseen rays.

With all my being I sensed, on that January day, how gentle was the south, how soft its air, how pleasant its humidity.

I had been to Sebastopol as a child, and again during the war, and now at a time of devastation and famine. Every time it seemed to me a new city, different from the one I had known before.

I wondered what it would be like when I saw it next – soon, I hoped. That I would see it again I felt sure. And indeed I was to come again often, and stay long, and become as attached to Sebastopol as to a second home. I am bound to it by many memories, of much grief and much happiness.

Were it not for Sebastopol, I would probably not have so vivid and, I believe, so exact a picture of those imaginary cities of Grin's[40] – his noisy Zurbagan and weed-grown Liss – towns which must undoubtedly exist somewhere in the universe.

Years of Hope

I was struck by the fact that on the blessed soil of Sebastopol even the lightest touch of the human hand could produce such attractive effects – unexpected alleyways and flights of stone steps drowning in wisteria, pleasantly winding roads, the swift play of sunlight on windows, balconies on which small lizards warmed themselves at midday, or the half-darkness and half-light of coffee houses with signboards daubed in watercolours like a child's painting.

For me, Sebastopol has never been quite real and part of prosy, everyday life.

Now and then, it seemed to me to be growing dull and grey, to have lost its picturesque landmarks. But at once the sight of the sea beyond the windows, or the smell of smoked *sultanka,* would bring me back to reality – to Sebastopol scattered like outcrops of ancient, yellowing marble on the shores of indigo bays, to the sound of its flags in the wind, to the phosphorescent flash of its oily waves, the smell of roses and tomatoes, and the visiting breeze from the far Aegean, drifting with its retinue of high pink clouds.

I watched Sebastopol for a long time from the stern of the *Pestel,* until at last we rounded the Khersones lighthouse and the lilac wall of the Crimean mountains rose on our port side.

Cold and excitement had kept me awake all night, so that now I could hardly keep my eyes open. I found a quiet, shady corner under the companionway in the saloon, lay down on the floor and fell asleep at once.

By the time I awoke, it was quite dark. The saloon, lit by a single bulb, smelt of sauerkraut.

I was seized with stomach cramps. Unbearably hungry, I shut my eyes to the horrifying prospect of total destitution and spent my last pennies on a plate of sauerkraut. I devoured it with the remaining crust of my one loaf of Sebastopol bread – it had lasted me till now.

On awakening I had thought it was night, but in fact it was only sunset. As though dripping with dark blood, the sheer cliffs of the Crimean range moved slowly and menacingly past the windows of the saloon. An unpleasantly sharp east wind was blowing on deck. Dull water, the colour of scum, flowed against the steamer. The cliffs of Yaila, rusty red with leafless oakwoods, glowed faintly here and there in the last light.

Far ahead, the Yalta lighthouse blinked its crimson eye. There was not one other light on the entire coast. The whole of the Crimea lay deserted, empty, swept by winter winds, numbed by the cold.

I looked hard at the shore, searching for at least a glimmer, however pitifully small – if only the flicker of a candle – to show that someone was still alive in that wilderness. But there was nothing – only the night swiftly falling and snuffing out the peaks of the mountains one by one.

We pulled in at Yalta at nine in the evening. The town was quiet and pitch dark. An occasional rifle shot came from the outskirts.

The pier was deserted. The wind ribbed the puddles and rolled empty barrels of sauerkraut; a few sentries in puttees and with shouldered rifles wandered about shivering.

We were told that the *Pestel* would stay at Yalta until morning, as it was dangerous to sail at night because of the mines. We could stretch our legs on the pier if we liked, but it was better not to go into town. There were no lights; on the other hand there were bandits; you risked being stopped at the very first crossroads and stripped naked or even killed.

'And if not by the bandits then by the Whites,' added a sentry who stood beside the gangway. 'They're skulking in the mountains, those who didn't get away in time. They've got their hide-outs up there. You'd have to burn them out with blowlamps.'

The Captain ordered the ship to be moved from the quayside and anchored a few yards away, so that no one could board her without being seen, but I had time to slip down to the pier, and walked towards the town gate.

When I came to it, I stopped. A flickering 'bat' oil lamp hung on the gate. An old man in a squashed naval cap sat on a box under the lamp, a rifle between his knees.

Years of Hope

Beyond the gate lay darkness. From it came an occasional rustle of dry leaves.

I walked on a few steps and stopped again. The watchman gave me a casual glance. It was all the same to him whether I was killed or not. All he wanted was that I shouldn't bother him with silly questions and distract him from thinking about his domestic affairs. He had seen plenty of killings, more than enough, and they no longer stirred him even to curiosity.

I looked back. I could still return to the ship, but an inexplicable excitement welled up in me. It was as though I were standing on the edge of a precipice.

I looked at the dim lights on the deck of the *Pestel,* and suddenly knew that I could not resist the call of the dark, that it was pulling me, that already I was more afraid of walking back, through the strip of solid shadow to the dim illumination of the pier, than of dissolving in that darkness and even of being killed in it.

I knew that I was foolishly tempting fate, that it was against all common sense to go into the town at night. But by now the darkness had me in its power. My heart pounding slowly, I persuaded myself that I could not go back until I had discovered what that watchful darkness concealed.

It happens, sometimes, that a man cannot recall the name of a place, or a date, or a surname, and until he does he is as one possessed, like a lunatic. He can think of nothing except the solution of the mystery, he becomes blind and deaf, and sees nothing around him. Something of the same sort had happened to me. The night held its secret, and I could not live until I had found the clue.

I was drawn to the darkness as French colonial soldiers are drawn to the Sahara. Babel had told me about them. They go off, deserting from their units, and never come back.

I had no fear. On the contrary, I longed for something to happen, immediate and decisive, that would settle my fate once and for all. It seemed to me that this night was a turning point in my life, that beyond it lay death or a blinding light.

I think now that my state in Yalta was the result of my hungry fortnight in Sebastopol. But at the time I was in it I could not be so objective.

Coolly and calmly I reminded myself how to behave in the dark – move silently, by stealth, hugging the walls, careful not to give myself away by so much as a sigh. The night was my cover. The only dangers (but they were mortal) were either a betraying sound – a cough, a shuffle, a wheezing breath, the crackle of a leaf underfoot – or actually stumbling into someone in the dark.

But as I reached the bridge over the dry bed of the river Uchan-Su, I realised that safety lay not in any of these precautions, but in my unfailing sense of the presence of those who, like me, were hiding in the dark. Every one of these invisible people was my enemy. Warned by my sixth or my twelfth sense – whatever it was, I possessed it – I knew that a few steps away a man stood listening. And although my hands were empty I felt, as he did, the steel rifle bolt warm from the contact of his hand.

My other advantage, and an enormous one at that, was that the enemies whom the pitch-black night concealed from me were ignorant of the first law of survival on such a night – perfect silence. So they often gave themselves away and I had time to avoid them.

It occurred to me that man is a much more noisy animal than we usually think. Even the movement of turning one's head, and still more one's whole torso, makes a sound which is sometimes plainly audible.

There was still another danger – matches. There were no electric torches at that time, but a match might flare at any moment and deliver me to sudden death.

Where was I going? I did not know until I came to a dead-end.

I walked for a long time, sometimes stepping into the roadway when for some reason the pavement seemed dangerous. Occasionally the wind rose and rustled in the cypresses, then I walked more boldly.

I avoided the edge of the pavement. There were vents in it for draining the rain-water.

Years of Hope

When exactly I came to a dead-end, I don't know. It must have been very late at night.

I walked into a stone wall. Another wall joined it on my left. I stretched up to feel the top, but could nowhere reach it.

On my right was still another wall. It was cut by a gate and, close to it, by a recess and a narrow wicket. Groping beside it, I found a name-plate.

This third wall was lower than the other two, it only came up to my shoulder. Beyond it I sensed that there was a thickly grown garden, although not a rustle came from it.

I took out my matches and struck three at once, so that the flame should be as bright as possible: I had decided to read the name on the plate.

By the light of the yellow flame I had time to read the words: *The House of Anton Pavlovich. . . .*

Then the matches blew out in the wind and, immediately, a shot came from somewhere above the Autsky highway. The bullet zoomed low over the wall, and with a soft crackle snapped a twig.

The second bullet went higher and was lost in the gloom in which lay the benumbed sea.

I squeezed myself into the recess of the wicket-gate. At once, everything was forgotten – my strange state, so like a sickness of the spirit, and the whole of my strenuous journey, as on a tight-rope, across the sinister town to this place, to Chekhov's house.

I had been to this house as a boy in 1906, two years after Chekhov's death, and had now come back after sixteen years.

Why I had come all the way to this remote suburb and to this particular house, I could not understand then, any more than I can today. I could not understand it, but of course it already seemed to me that I had come deliberately, that I had known my destination, that I had something urgent on my mind which had brought me here.

What could this be?

Suddenly and deeply, I felt the bitterness and pain of all I had lost in life. I thought of my mother and Galya,[41] of their dual, undeserved love for me, burning somewhere far away; of Lena;

of the attentive, tired eyes of Chekhov looking through his pince-nez. I pressed my face against the stone wall and, trying hard not to, wept all the same.

I wished the gate would creak open, and Chekhov come out and ask me what was wrong.

I raised my head. Pale in the darkness, the mountains shone with a magical and steady light. I guessed that snow had fallen on them – crisp dry mountain snow that crunches underfoot like gravel.

And suddenly I felt the nearness and certainty of happiness. Why, I don't know. Perhaps because of that pure snow-whiteness which looked like the distant radiance of a beautiful country, or because of my sense of sonship – long unexpressed and driven to the back of my mind – towards Russia, towards Chekhov. He had loved his country in many ways, and he had loved her as the shy bride about whom he wrote his last story. He had firmly believed that she was going unwaveringly towards justice, beauty and happiness.

I, too, believed in that happiness – that it would come to my country, to starved and frozen Crimea, and also to me. I felt this as a swift and joyful impulse, like a passionate look of love. It warmed my heart and dried my tears of loneliness and fatigue.

I made no attempt to hide on my way back. Twice I was shot at. At last, still in the same inky darkness, I passed the old man sitting with his rifle at the gate, and he gave me the same casual glance as he had several hours earlier.

For a long time I sat on the pier, leaning against one of the square blocks of cement of which it was built, and watched the night turn grey, and waited for the *Pestel* to pull in at the quayside. Then I would go back to my corner under the companionway in the saloon, and sleep. And even asleep, as always in my waking hours, I would wait for happy, unpredictable changes and events.

Notes

1 Ilf: pseudonym of I. A. Feinzilberg (1897–1931), co-author with Petrov of satirical novels *Twelve Chairs* (1928) and *The Golden Calf* (1931); author of *Notebooks* published posthumously in 1939.

2 Ostap Bender: racketeer, comic hero of *Twelve Chairs*.

3 *Bourzhouika:* 'housewife' – nickname given to small metal stove.

4 *Russian Word:* daily paper with a very large circulation, published in Moscow, 1894–1917.

5 Odessa grew from a small town to one of the largest Russian cities in the late 18th and early 19th centuries. The city and port were planned by J. Deribas (b. in Naples, 1749, d. 1800), who took service in the Russian forces and rose to be General, then Admiral. Armand, Duc de Richelieu (1766–1822), a French emigré, was Governor of Odessa until his return to France at the Restoration. The architecture is Western; there is a monument to Richelieu and streets named after Richelieu and Deribas.

6 Cheka: 'Special Commission' – original name of Soviet Security Service, now the K.G.B.

7 A. I. Denikin (1872–1947) Tsarist General in command of the Southern Front during the Civil War; formed the (White) 'Volunteer Army' and, with the aid of the Entente forces, twice occupied Odessa; defeated in 1920, emigrated to England.

8 Wild lands: region of Ukraine over-run by White and Ukranian nationalist bands under rival chiefs.

9 Valentin Katayev, b. 1897, novelist.

10 The Poles, fighting Russia for the territories they had lost to her in the 17th century, occupied Kiev and were expelled by the Red Army under General Budenny in 1920.

11 Tsaddic: Jewish sage.

12 Baron P. N. Vrangel (1878–1928), General who commanded the White Volunteer Army in the Crimea; defeated in 1920 and emigrated.

Notes

13 Plyushkin: miser in Gogol's *Dead Souls*.

14 Bagritsky: pseudonym of Edward Dzubin (1895–1934), poet, strongly influenced by the revolutionary-romantic style of the early twenties.

15 Fet: pseudonym of A. A. Shenshin (1820–92), lyrical poet. I. I. Brodsky: (1883–1939), realist painter on historical themes.

16 New Economic Policy (NEP): policy of economic relaxation which favoured the peasants and was ended by Stalin soon after Lenin's death.

17 Itinerants: realistic school of painters who organised itinerant exhibitions (1870–1923).

18 I. E. Repin (1844–1930), leading Itinerant painter.

19 The immediate effect of the NEP was to relieve the food shortage in the towns.

20 I. G. Babel (1894–1941), outstanding short-story writer; died in a concentration camp.

21 Babel fought in General Budenny's Cavalry Corps campaign against the Poles in 1920; he described it in his famous collection of short stories *Cavalry Corps*.

22 A. A. Blok (1880–1921): greatest Russian poet of his time. Wrote lyrical, mystical, symbolical verse; welcomed the revolution in his poem *The Twelve*.

23 Sasha Cherny: pseudonym of A. M. Glikberg (1880–1932), satirical poet.

24 I. M. Moskvin (1874–1946), famous actor.

25 Samuel Marshak (1887–1966), Children's writer, lyrical and satirical poet, author of Memoirs.

26 *Zembussar*: derisory term for those who avoided military service on the pretext of serving in local voluntary, semi-military organisations.

27 Igor Severyanin: pseudonym of I. V. Lotarev (1887–1942), 'ego-futurist' poet very popular during the First War; emigrated to Esthonia but returned when it was occupied by the Soviet Union in 1940.

28 S. I. Kirsanov (b. 1906), poet.

29 I. K. Aïvazovsky (1817–1900), painter of sea-scrapes.

Notes

30 'Luminous': the Russian word *luchezarny*, made up of *luch* – ray – and *zarya* – dawn or dusk, has no exact equivalent in English.

31 A. I. Kuprin (1870–1938), novelist and short story writer; emigrated in 1917, returned in 1939.

32 Sakhalin: island off east coast of Asia, used as convict settlement in Tsarist times.

33 Susanin: Patriotic hero of Glinka's Opera, *A Life for the Tsar*.

34 Girl poet: Paustovsky met her when he visited Sebastopol on the eve of the February Revolution (*Slow Approach of Thunder*).

35 Hessian fly: nickname given to the Empress Alexandra who was born Princess Alice of Hesse.

36 M. Vrubel (1856–1910), painter, friend of Paustovsky's father (*Childhood and Schooldays*). M. A. Voloshin (1878–1932), poet whom Paustovsky met in Moscow in 1917 (*In that Dawn*). I. A. Bunin (1817–1953), novelist (*Slow Approach of Thunder*). The rest are friends and acquaintances described in previous volumes.

37 Alexander Pushkin (1799–1837), probably the greatest Russian poet, author of *Eugene Onegin*, etc. V. A. Zhukovsky (1783–1852), romantic poet.

38 Admiral A. V. Kolchak (1873–1920), in command of White Army which occupied Siberia and advanced West, reaching the Volga; defeated and shot in February 1920.

39 F. A. Rubo (1856–1928), painter of '*Defense of Sebastopol*'.

40 Grin: pseudonym of A. S. Grinevsky (1880–1932), novelist.

41 Galya: Paustovsky's sister.